MOUNTAINHEAD

. . . . . .

NEW JUCHE

NINE-BANDED
BOOKS

Mountainhead

© 2017 New Juche

Published by

Nine-Banded Books
PO Box 1862
Charleston, WV 25327
www.NineBandedBooks.com

ISBN 10: 0990733564
ISBN 13: 978-0990733560

Editorial Assistance:
Anita Dalton, James Nulick

Cover design by Kevin I. Slaughter

Mountainhead

A good beginning to this might be a habit I developed back home, watching a group of local homosexuals going in and out of a public toilet at the foot of Calton Hill. The hill itself, with its trees, towers and monuments, was used at night for various forms of sinister faggot trade, and was in the popular imagination a dangerous, off-limits location, an impression that was fueled by successive rumours of murder and sexual violence that included notorious policemen, politicians and other corrupt local celebrities. By day though, only tourists climbed to its peak to photograph the views and the massive, unfinished monument known as 'Edinburgh's Disgrace.'

The toilet was located where the foot of the hill meets the corner of Easter and London Road, set back off the pavement at the top of some steps and partially obscured by hedges and a row of bus shelters. The small building served as a rough-trade drop-in centre for a community of mentally and physically disabled male perverts. I first discovered this one afternoon as I sat at the nearest bus stop to the structure, idly noting the presence of a Down syndrome man in a stained blue anorak designed for a woman, hovering at the entrance with a cigarette. Presently another short, bald man with a speech impediment climbed the steps and addressed the other—

—Huv ye been in? Are ye gaun in?

Down syndrome turned in silence and skulked into the toilet, followed by the bald man. Fascinated, I waited to see them coming out but after a few minutes my bus arrived. After this, I went to stand at the same bus stop several times a week, watching similar interactions between similar creatures. A few of them were clearly very seriously ill, all swollen limbs and red faces with cracked, peeling skin. The toilet was a chapel, the hill behind it a cosmology of perversion and sexual crime.

The religious and sexual possibilities of *forest* here in upland Southeast Asia, aside from a visionary rubric of the ascetic ideal – being lost, mastering fear and magic and so on – can be understood in terms of the sensory cacophony that the environment is made up from. The endless forms and colours of semi-deciduous broadleaf, the dizzying perfumes and stenches, and a soundscape so rich and dynamic in timbre even within its quite separate genres of birdsong, insects, frogs, water and trees. This forest, this mountain, is also covered in decayed and rotting anthropomorphic secrets because the apparatus of the state is limited in its reach here. Traditionally the forest has offered the lowland natives of this territory a degree of privacy unavailable in their actual living spaces or elsewhere. It cultivates the illicit. I pick a matt-purple insect off a rubbery leaf and it shoots a thick jet of coppery urine across my arm, and I'm provoked by the sexual implications of it. This work should be classified as part of the MOUNTAIN CRIMES genre.

I've never thought my sexuality or my sexual behaviour and its motivations to be static in essence, although there are a number of themes that emerged both before and during adolescence that have retained their centrality. Nor has this evolution, or 'lack of stasis,' been driven by a process of desensitisation – I now have less contact with other human beings than I ever did before, but that is immaterial because I never used to distinguish between prostitutes and pornography. The point is that the themes seem endlessly to re-present themselves to me in different contexts.

I like repetition, and I think it's a truly crucial element to art, and to developing criteria, a means of seeing and understanding. Often a single image or two washes through an artist's career, and it's all the key and context that was necessary for the artist to realise the world. The first copy of *Escort Reader's Wives* given to me by a school friend, along with a cache of nazi patches and stickers, was the most valuable collection of photographs I ever owned in my life. I say that now in full confidence almost thirty years later, but even then it stood out from the other material that passed along with copper coins and cigarettes through our grimy hands. The porn that lay around outside the gypsy camp behind my scheme with its leather and vaginas and sex-shop adultness, its sneering women and their alien bodies, painted and dusted and disturbing; it was very exciting but not arousing in the acutely perfect fashion that *Escort* was. The stodgy schoolteacher shape of the *Escort* women and their breasts, their amiable expressions and housewife good humour, that was for me very much about favours delivered with indulgence and in the total absence of female sexuality, a mothering village prostitute whose engorged and dangling bare breasts were all I needed, maybe a game of kiss-chase for variety, or a Ronnie Barker postcard-style rape fantasy. Like all magazine pornography in that time most of it was sliced up, traded and destroyed, but I still have its most important relics preserved in a scrapbook, and I still use the power of those relics to come inside real women today.

I used to masturbate to a very short video I downloaded randomly of a young, tanned woman with large breasts removing her top on a beach. The footage looked like it had been shot without her knowledge, and her naked breasts were only visible for four and a quarter seconds. I tried pausing the video at the moment where the full weight and shape is best conveyed through the camera, but it didn't work – within the context of this material's sexual value, and my masturbation to it, the paused still image wasn't exciting. It was better to just let the video run on a loop, as though I had no control.

I remember with great fondness photographs of an *Escort Reader's Wives* model called Phillippa. She was an old woman, in her sixties, with large, milky-white breasts and pink nipples which she offered to the camera with a teasing, slightly haughty confidence, or indolently let dangle like big wonderful udders while she peered down her nose at the camera. Who's going to make Phillippa a cup of tea? It was the first time I developed a deep sexual relationship with an image of a person who didn't conform at all to the prescribed conventions of my peer group, and I felt shameful about masturbating to Phillippa at first. I diligently collected *Escort* and other similar magazines, which through their celebratory language and presentation quickly extinguished the feelings of transgression. Phillippa's oldness wasn't what made her breasts desirable in the first instance; it was the breasts that somehow transferred some of their desirability on to her oldness. But her oldness in turn served to sexualise the context her breasts appeared in to an even more heightened degree. I still have two creased and faded photographs of Phillippa stuck in a scrapbook, alongside other ugly, obese and elderly women with big breasts.

I like seeing foreign women's breasts revealed in non-sexual contexts, as can often be seen in slums, rural settlements and villages across tropical Asia. Usually it's breastfeeding mothers, but the most refined pleasure for me is in plump, sour-faced, middle-aged women waddling around topless in their open-front hovels.

The initial reason I came to live so close to the mountain was that one of my primary research sites was located near its peak. The Hmong village there is the most accessible highlander community in this region, settled permanently in the fifties and subject to a number of externally sponsored development projects. Twenty clicks up the mountain from the city, the misty village sits in the basin of a small valley with views across the range.

The present era began whilst I was reviewing the photos from my second or third research trip, and I noticed a woman breastfeeding in front of her house in the periphery of one shot. The side of her breast was clearly defined and she was looking just to the right of me, not at the camera. I felt a charge looking at the shot and surprise that I hadn't noticed her at the time. The picture inspired me to masturbate to two other topless photographs of a squat foreign woman I'd taken a few years before. The two were my favourite from a series of nine, and had to be retrieved from the original folder I'd created to keep them in and placed side by side on my computer screen. These efforts should be understood as part of a fine-grained, interdisciplinary study of *mountain-relief*.

Of course the picture was enough to inspire return breast-watching trips to the village, which quickly became a regular fixture in my week. In the late stages of its permanent settlement in the eighties, the village bifurcated into an 'authentic' zone for Caucasian tourists and a hidden or disguised private zone where residents actually lived. As the trade done in the authentic zone became increasingly busy and less authentic in the eyes of foreign tourists, the village evolved further into an actual showcase for state development projects rather than an authentic primitive experience. The old museums with their signs in English have fallen into disrepair, whilst the contrived and prosaic flower garden and its irrigation reservoir full of naked brown children is busy all day with domestic tourists from the city and beyond. What used to be the authentic zone is now a paved network of shops and restaurants selling replica tat and packaged forest products, and the residential side is accessible to anyone who cares to wander into it. The Hmong live, do business and recreate under a constant tourist gaze, which they have apparently grown completely indifferent to.

Hmong women are quite remarkable to look at with their squat forms and taut, ochre skin. Most have breasts like conical bulbs that sprout from either side of their barrel-like trunks, others carry these thick, floppy, latex sacks of liquid that seem to start from their collarbones and taper down into two acute points. There's a vegetable quality to them. Older women are the most striking, some with huge, elegant turbans and thin-lensed spectacles resting above flat nostrils. Women breastfeed everywhere but the doors of most dwellings are left wide open anyway, and as I have some legitimate reason to be interested and to take pictures, I can, and I do.

Every opportunity is exploited to make money from visitors, and many houses and shops advertise the use of their toilet holes for five baht a go. And so, the necessary environment and facilities are in place for a ritualised, highly structured and fussy template of behaviour that has followed me from the port of Leith to continental Europe, all over southern and central Siam, former Indochina and now here. In Leith I stalked the cold docks and industrial estates in a leather jacket with concern and purpose, mostly just watching street-walkers and then masturbating in a stairwell or behind a row of bins. In Amsterdam I prowled and window-shopped, very consciously enjoying the interaction with the space and its contents, before I sort of peaked and either knocked on a glass door or rented a private video booth.

I like spatial diagrams and maps of red-light areas in academic studies, both appropriated places and those that are purpose-built. I love that I can enter the Klong on Google Street View and look at the women sitting on plastic chairs along the pavement.

I usually park my bike way back down the deep forest trail and walk into the village at some point after noon, sipping white spirit from a plastic bottle in an absurd state of excitement. With its mixture of market, sun-bleached iron slum, pleasure garden, farm and forest, I find the location heady and stimulating in its own right, and can happily spend hours loitering in its variety, waiting for the partial glimpse of udder that is nothing short of religious in its capacity to trigger the most powerful and catastrophic spasms of childish sexual fury. Once one of these is upon me I politely pay my way into somebody's home, beat off into their toilet, and sling my hook.

The turning point in my relationship with the mountain that I wish to discuss occurred one late afternoon as I was heading home from the village. The wide, sweeping road is downhill all the way and I let my bike glide down with the engine off, enjoying the trees and smells and patches of hot and cold air. Touts and taxi drivers hover in groups on both sides of the road by the temple staircase, thinning out past the food carts and the jade workshop. And this is how the curse of love smiled out at me. She sat on a concrete ledge between two fat women, her pink t-shirt cradling obscenely full, perfectly round breasts: *a beautiful, armless Hmong dwarf*. She wore the smile of a deity and her black eyes were shiny with mucous. Her little arm-stubs were like handles on the side of a stout clay pot. My reeling mind and body thumped with the chemicals of confused desire and my vision began to pixelate into grey and I thought if I came off the bike it would easily be more than the stimulus required to spontaneously ejaculate. I imagined myself twisted and bleeding on the road a few feet from the bike, skinless knees and forearms, sperm-smeared erection poking out horribly from my open trousers.

I let the bike roll a respectable couple of clicks down the road and then turned into a small car park that served one of the platformed viewpoints that looks out over the province. I made my way down into the concrete bunker-toilet below the platform and into the cubicle, undid my belt and let my trousers and boxer shorts fall round my ankles. There was some gay graffiti written in Thai on the stone.

WHO LIKES TO SUCK BIG COCKS? I HAVE A MONSTER COCK. I WILL TAKE IT AND SUCK IT. WHO LIKES BIG COCKS? FAGGOTS. I LOVE SUCKING COCKS. DO YOU WANT YOUR COCK SUCKED OFF? I'LL BE HERE EVERY SATURDAY AND SUNDAY AT FIVE.

My cock seemed so hard that it had lost all sensitivity. I pounded on it and tried to focus on images and ideas but nothing seemed to work. No single image in the kaleidoscope would melt through into being the subject of focus. I finally got in the right gear by thinking about the village again and came powerfully into a wet wipe, which I folded up into a little parcel and threw in the bucket beside the toilet bowl.

Obtaining and preparing food takes up a disproportionate percentage of my time, as I no longer eat in restaurants or buy prepared food of any kind. I do buy some raw supplies from the various markets around the lodge, which operate at different times and sell different types of food. I regularly buy small sacks of wholemeal rice, sesame, dried chillis, wild honey collected in old rum bottles, fermented fish sauce for calcium and salt, fermented bean curd, and, depending on price and availability, various types of fish, prawns, crabs, squid, frogs, chicken and occasionally pork. I usually hoard dried fish and prawns, carefully sealed in plastic and hidden from ants, and feel an enhanced sense of security when my stocks are full. I am almost fully indebted to the forest for fruit, herbs and vegetables, and am constantly in awe of the variety and quality of what appears to be randomly growing around the lodge, let alone up and into the mountain proper. My 'garden,' so to speak, provides wild lemongrass, ginger, peppercorns, lime leaves, coriander, betel leaves and other herbs, stubby little bananas, papaya, sour mangos, rose-apples, fans of blade-like pandan leaves which I've learnt to infuse in water, and large, pale limes whose rinds are so porous and sensitive that their fragrance dances on my fingers for hours after picking them. These flavours and scents, the trills and flourishes of their variations, come together to form a rural perfume, an essence, which I imagine passes through the pores of my own skin, just as the odour of fir sap permeates from the cold trees of my childhood.

I've been drawing maps of specific parts of the mountain, particularly the Hmong village, and marking on them details of significance and importance to me. For my convenience and satisfaction. When I began my research I acquired all the maps I could find of the village and its surrounds, including a military map of this half of the mountain range, but none of them plot out the exact trails and paths of the rapidly expanding village itself. I've made two maps of the village, both works in progress. The first is a broad and rough line diagram of the whole location, for reference. It's not to scale, but it helps me to see how the separate areas I've identified are linked. The second is a detailed representation of the 'centre,' by which I mean the commercial and residential zones in which most tourist foot traffic circulates. Peripheral spaces such as the school, the flower garden and the forest trails are not included. This map is marked with all the toilets accessible to the public in the centre, most importantly the ones in private homes. Each private toilet is heavily annotated.

SIGNS

How big is the sign?

What language, font and colour is it written in? (Eighty percent in Siamese, conservative font, red ink. Sometimes the words TOILET FIVE BAHT are daubed in white paint across corrugated iron with an arrow pointing to the door.)

What is the exact wording of the sign and how much is access to the toilet being advertised for? (They are all five baht.)

Where on the house is the sign and how visible is it from the street?

HOUSE

(The residential zone has all sorts of housing, and is growing in all directions at a steady pace. It must still be classified as *slum* or *shanty town*, that is to say, pure functionality with no aesthetic consideration, and the minimal utilisation of the cheapest, most convenient materials. A close examination shows the housing to reflect the lowland social values and organisation imposed on the Hmong; the Headman's house, whilst not the biggest or newest, has encroached on its previously occupied surrounds through a gradual but assertive process of colonisation. Space has been cleared to accommodate his family's growing collection of vehicles, which include two brand new ISUZU pick-ups. His television and other consumer goods are prominently displayed like austere sentinels. Much of the community live in shacks or long-houses of wood, tyres and corrugated iron. Spirit houses and Buddhist altars, in a comparatively spartan style, are evidenced in and outside most domiciles.)

Is the door usually open or shut?

Describe the domicile, giving details of the size, contents, smells, quality of light and inhabitants.

What are the inhabitants doing? e.g., eating, preparing food, sleeping, playing, engaged in cottage-industry production, needlework, etc.

Toilet

Is the toilet partitioned from the rest of the room with wood or corrugated iron, and how wide are the spaces between the partitioning material and the floor and ceiling respectively?

Is it possible to see outside the building from within the toilet? If so, what can be seen and how well?

What are the dimensions of the toilet?

Is the convenience itself a simple hole in the ground or a porcelain squat toilet mounted on a concrete block?

Is there a tap or water-source in the toilet other than the flushing bucket?

Is there soap or paper? (There never is.)

How would the maintenance and cleanliness of the toilet be described?

These annotations allow me to plot out on paper and therefore in my memory exactly where the nearest toilet is and what I can expect from it, wherever I am in the village. I can make informed aesthetic decisions about which toilet will best complement the subject I wish to masturbate to. There is no useful system for marking these subjects themselves on the map. Their appearance and value occur arbitrarily in relation to this exercise. At this stage however, having gained a temporal, experiential perspective, meaningful patterns have emerged.

The Dwarf's *ism* or essence, her full range of meaning and effect, is something that I feel viscerally, rather than understand intellectually. That is to say, that I find the words which report to my command in service of an explanation are inadequate. I hope that in the act of writing this monograph I will firstly arrive at some definitions and develop them through a plotted history of intention, action and consequence. To that end I have coined the term *Dwarfology*, for use here as a touchstone, compass, spade and mirror. This work should be classified as the first part of a gazetteer of location-specific Asian *Dwarfology*.

The following morning I rose early and cut wood for a fire to barbecue the small freshwater fish I'd bartered from a neighbour. After breakfast I put the remainder of the meat in an envelope of glutinous rice to take with me for lunch up the mountain. I set off on my bike around ten. I knew there was no possibility of talking to the Dwarf today, the thing was going to take a lot of time, months, and I was perfectly happy and suited to that. Even the thought of eye contact delivered rushes of anxiety. I had my walking trousers on and my mountain jacket with a hat in the pocket in case it rained. In other pockets I had a notebook, camera, tobacco and wet wipes. On the way round to the mountain road I filled the tank with petrol and had the boy pour some surplus in a plastic bottle for me.

I internally spatialise the road by dividing it into stages, based on specific landmarks like entrances or side roads leading off to temples or waterfalls, research stations, public toilets, religious billboards, or stretches of a particular type or composition of forest, and the parts of the road that veer into sharp or sweeping corners, or from which there are views. With each passing stage my excitement grew, and so the gamut of possibilities seemed to also. I might stop and whittle a stick into a smooth phallus and work it into my rectum. Of course that would qualify as a *Dwarfological* act. At one point, misguided by fear, I even convince myself the best thing to do would just be to head back down into town and spend the day drinking in brothels. Just before reaching the fount and seat of *Dwarfology* there is a very acute corner on a steep gradient. As I lean round the corner into view of the Dwarf's ledge my heart contracts with disappointment, but not with surprise. I park my bike.

I crouch in front of the empty ledge and bask in my proximity to the space she so recently occupied. I train my eyes on the exact area in the air which I believe was filled by her immortal bulbs, and I actually feel physical sensation in my penis as I push my face towards and into that space, the skin that covers my nose and cheeks feels magnetised, hungrily reaching out to be touched. I can feel myself being filled up like a tank. And out from this communion I rise into the giddy anticipation and charged remove of concentrated *Dwarfological* intent.

I power up the road and bring my machine to a controlled stop one hundred meters from the village entrance, under the cover of leaf and mist. I'm a shanty-town masturbation-commando. I open the plastic bottle and huff some gasohol 95. I stretch out my arms like a deformed swan and glide up the track drooling and drunk on the smell of earth and wet trees. *Dwarfology* imbues all stimulus and action with a sense of destiny and the profound, and as I'm born into the sudden light of the village it feels like a great homecoming. I walk deliberately and slowly into a crowded tunnel of corrugated iron and concrete. Children and chickens envelop me into their flow and a toothless old man smoking a pipe in an armchair stares right through me into the past. A large wooden building in front of me has a toilet sign above an open door, through which I have an impression of female activity and smells. I raise my hands together respectfully and slowly enter the house. Five beautiful old Hmong women are cooking food on an open fire in the middle of the room. They look at me in unison and I swoon in the embrace of their scrutiny. The dark room smells of charcoal and the meat stew they're making. I ask for the toilet and the woman nearest the wooden cubicle door leans over quite unnecessarily and swishes it open in a gesture of goodwill as they continue clucking in their mountain tongue. I walk carefully over the bumpy stone-cobbled floor and into the wooden cubicle feeling transported through the leaden cow's breath of the Dwarf.

Inside the cubicle, which has no lock but does have a high window letting in the severe grey of the sky, I unzip and pull out my erection. The head is extra sensitive as I roll back my foreskin, exposing it to the thick air. My mind spins as I arch my back and beat my hard, supporting the posture with my left hand against a plank of weathered wood that forms a section of the partition. I usually come very quickly in these toilets, but I feel I'm a long way off, and pause to try and catch an image. I squeeze the shaft of my cock in protest as they flit across my mind like a manic slideshow, out of control. I think of a small brown girl with huge, round butterballs with no visible nipples. I need a curvy hairless body without a face, nipples or a vagina. Just two large, round, perfectly smooth breasts. Minutes pass as I start-stoppingly pump and stroke and beat and my frustration grows. I pinch my nipples with my left hand and then cup my scrotum and yank as hard as I can. One of the women comes close to the unlocked door and asks me if I'm ok. I say yes but my stomach is giving me trouble. A few more minutes. Take your time she says. My cock is sore with friction burns and bleeding a little. I attempt once more to yield, holding a wet wipe to catch the sperm with my left hand as a psychological spur, but in spite of its undying hardness I feel nothing. Blood and images gallop through my mind. I drop the wet wipe and carefully tuck my engorged organ back into my trousers and under my belt, then noisily pour a few buckets of water into the squat toilet. Outside the women smile and peer at me through inquisitive slits as I try to finger the change out of my wallet with sweaty hands. Embarrassingly I can only find four baht, which the women accept with laughter.

I feel desperate as I stagger through the chickens and the tourist car park and back under the dark relief of the canopy again. Twenty yards along the road or so I stop and look back furtively before climbing up the sodden bank between tight clumps of bamboo. I exclaim in panic as I walk into thick spiderweb and lose my footing to some treacherous frond, down into the paste. I sit still for a moment and listen to insects drone and the echo of birdsong. The white mist on the road is just visible through the bamboo but otherwise I'm cloaked in seething shadow. I lie on my back, take out my erection and carefully arrange my fingers in a grip that doesn't aggravate the friction burns. Beating through the pain like a sick addict I finally experience a sensationless and almost totally dry orgasm, and then sink down into a vacant doze.

Something on my face makes me sit up with a start, and this activates a rash of mosquito bites all over my body. I'm sticky and thirsty as I pull a small leech from my hip. My penis is so tender and raw it's difficult to walk. Back out on the paved road I feel and see myself and what I've done today with startling clarity under the tall trees. Straddling my bike not without difficulty, I start the engine and move off slowly.

The reader may be disgusted by my behaviour and its rubric, and feel that I am defiling the mountain like a piece of grit in your eye. But I belong now in this place, I'm attached to it. The mountain dictates my behaviour as the soil does a worm's. Can you understand that? What I'm doing here is valid and harmonious.

The reasons in my leaving Bangkok for the north were in part circumstantial, and it's only now that I'm ensconced in my surroundings here that the departure has become reclassified as a driven exodus. A city is always a mental product, but the event of the exodus has drawn out both richer pictures of evil, and more concentrated strains of nostalgia in my estrangement from it. At the beginning, in the city, I was unable to arrest all the beauty around me in some essential way. I found it very difficult to separate and focus. I felt the most satisfaction lying in bed with the noises of the city outside, breathing its air, idly assembling narratives, images and locations in my mind, and toying with the simple fact of where I was and what I could do there. I liked to make plans for going to favoured locations and just taking photographs. The places I liked best were made impenetrable by photographs. The pictures formed a smooth rippling skin over their subjects that I liked to rub up against. (Likewise in Hanoi, interred in the cool air of a tall townhouse, I would repeat the name of the city and the country over and over like a mantra, nourishing the physical inactivity of what a friend called my *empty life* with the images and essences that those names evoked.)

Looking now at my photos, I can obviously pare down with accuracy the basic elements I was feeding from in the city. I used to just buy disposable cameras then, and most of the pictures I took with them are worthless. I had no notion of composition or the way light could or could not be captured, and I gave no real consideration to my subjects. I knew where I was but didn't know what I should be looking for, and would simply allow myself to be guided into bed by the first working person to proposition me. I was maybe, actually, a bit flattered by the sales line, certainly inhibited in expressing my needs or tastes. So I would put off taking pictures of the places I really wanted to own images of. I would work towards them so to speak, identify my real targets as I let go my teeth into the closest bait at any given time. My tastes fell into the background, and I became a much younger man. Pointing my camera at an old woman sitting on the ground behind a swarm of flies that veil the pile of putrid fish she's selling, and having her lick and nuzzle the lens. I'll come back. I'll come again. But I never would, and I knew I never would. As I wandered around, the ignorance of a single one being every one started to break apart and I got a sense of the interior. The thing I was most preoccupied with owning, that I most wanted a photograph of, that I was able to masturbate to the idea of photographing, and that honestly used to make me spontaneously ejaculate in my trousers when I saw in real life, on really very many occasions, was a topless fat woman in an alleyway, not prostitutes. That's it, that's perfection, that's going a long way toward perfection. I call it the rapture, when all these contrived efforts give way suddenly to something truly valuable, to keep and look for more of.

The Fat Ladyboy lived a very courageous life dedicated unconditionally to her sexuality. Her every thought and action was in service to it. Her working altar was a small, private hole filled with pornography, make-up and other dedicated paraphernalia to which she offered herself constantly. I know because I have been there and taken hundreds of photographs of her smooth, plump, naked body. She had made a personal history of her she-male-ism that contained important memories of events and sensations. These memories had hardened into anachronistic themes and motifs that entwined themselves retrospectively into the history, setting its course into some parallel linear shapes and reproducing into the present. In the southern jungle as a young boy she had loved her brother. The jungle is a place of secrets and illicit behaviour, and her brother and his friends often took her with them to shoot birds and toss off. She didn't enjoy hunting or fighting other boys, but as a youth it was her duty and she performed it out of filial obligation. After killing animals the group would split up with a magazine or photograph, to masturbate. Resting her left hand flat against the trunk of a big tree, the Fat Ladyboy imagined sucking the cocks of her brother and his friends right there in the forest as she pulled on herself. (At night, the Fat Ladyboy told me, she would grapple with and masturbate at terrible urges to go into her brother's corner as he slept, to kiss and worship his penis.)

I have recorded hours of interviews with the Fat Ladyboy. She neatly and expediently understood what I was doing as being something that served her own needs – she took direction from me naked, her little penis taut and furious with embarrassment. The camera was an early Nikon digital. In insufficient light and without the flash it would render each picture an impressionistic blur of reds and oily yellows. It also opened the shutter perhaps over a second after the button had been pressed, with the result that my puerile compositions of porno poses were disconfigured by the delay. The camera could never keep up with either of us, especially once we'd gathered a momentum. These two unintended effects are what make this series of pictures so distinct from all my other bad photography.

The Fat Ladyboy's rollicking buttocks, rolls of red flesh and podgy arms perform a disobedient ballet of physical language in a timeless and highly artificial environment. The stain of me *is there* though. I know the pseudo-academic, tucked-in shirt of a blur in the mirror is I, holding my camera. And in the hieroglyphs of its limbs, the prestige and frequency of its dry, bulbous tits – in spite of the camera's lucky corruption of my instructions – that is also me. And on my computer screen now as I look through these, I see my own cock hanging, rudely, between its two big shanks. I'd much rather suck my own cock through some surrogate if I could. With a lot of these creatures, I got my cock out as I photographed, just pulled down my trousers and boxer shorts to expose it, and sometimes when I didn't they would suggest the idea themselves, so it became a convention. Once quite a nice one walked out of the hotel room leaving me like that as I called her back, after she'd hurriedly taken many photographs of my exposed cock on her phone. I'd asked her if she'd ever been raped, and from that point on our contrived exchange had begun to unravel into loaded misunderstandings.

But the Fat Ladyboy was a big, meaty lump of a man. I had to start off small, with thin girly waifs of ladyboys. I remember over-enthusiastically necking this lanky, skeletal youth called Pinkie and letting him slurp all up and down at my cock with doubtful experience. It really was just a skinny Asian man in a dress. My best friend Pod encouraged it, and I saw it frankly as a rite of passage attached to the location and lifestyle, though I'd all but forgotten my teenage forbidden handjob expeditions to Amsterdam. Pod spent a lot of his time engaged in the hobby, and building a quiet wall of preemptive justification based on why men who didn't share these tastes and experiences were blind to certain facts. Quite a lot, their cocks are shrunken and inert from hormones, which suited Pod. The delightfully bad surgery used to be my favourite, and also seemed much more pictur-esque, and more responsive to the cruelty of intention I aspired to as a photographer. Like they've cut and ob-scenely ruined their bodies deliberately just to become or even just to vaguely resemble a third or beyond rate, last-chance, five a.m. coin-operated toilet. Prostitute. How I love that word. And this so quickly turns to ad-miration when you learn more about their natures, their courage, and how truly thrilling and satisfying it can be to have one suck you off while you're out of your mind on filthy meth. Imagine that you're entrusting your-self, turning your self over to them and open into really hours and hours of nude sessions of cumming. Then they re-emerge and reassemble themselves into a new value system. They are saintly, but the arietta is a short one and gave way quickly enough to bigger cocks and smaller tits. Less bad surgery scars, unnatural lumps and ridges and asymmetry. More lazy, out of shape men in padded bras and barely feminine dress. But I really do see *my* cock adhered there. As long as I used what-ever exact words and phrases – it is one thing and not another – I received my permissions.

Up here on the mountain I feel little compulsion for this shit anymore. Pod called it liberation, but I don't find it liberating; I find it paints me into a corner ulti-mately. But it was worth it then for the files and files of photographs, the videos and the other proof. It's all so perfect like this in a way, the happy accident, of my in-hibition, especially in retrospect. Who would I be now if I were truly courageous like Pod? A significant de-tail is that I used to write Pod out of this whole thing, but his memory is just as subjective as mine despite its Apollonian disposition, and in the end it's the photos that are real and permanent. They exist, and I will make captions and write redacted narratives that serve them, until a better method presents itself.

In one, the Fat Ladyboy's flesh is blown up in marbled swathes of overlapping dark reds. The shapes echo and reverberate out of focus, are squeezed, stretched, twisted and mangled bits of hair-gristle, dribble, lollop, float apart like lazy clouds and back to concentrate into the deepest clefts of dry crimson and muscular bubblegum from which I can smell the sickly, shit-sweet yeast and talcum. Happily, through my indecision at the time, I switched the flash on and off arbitrarily, allowing myself a comparison in review. With the flash on, there is his naked body and fake tits, there it is: plump and revolting. With it off, her body is blown apart into red light. Delayed close-ups occasion total somatic shift. In another one, I clasp her folded wings together with the elbows about to meet above head, vertically, in a nearly Gothic arch of taut flesh. Some fine metallic wisps of hair, hands like flattened spiders cover face, folded into the great arch with fibrous dimples and sinew, to come up as rearing hulk: the head of a marine mammal, emerged out from any focus, maritime colossus, ugly dolphin-lipped elbow-nose pointing at the circular basket of ceiling fan, on the overhanging grid of ceiling tiles. The image is pulverising. There is an inhuman grin if you want (maybe no one would see it but I) cut through the fish-head and essentially separate from the Fat Ladyboy, whose facial essence is better collected with pouty fidelity in dolphin-nose.

In another, it poses woman-like at mirror. What a mirror – a horizontal shaft of image better defined than the content of the room in which it hangs. But the room. The fucked-up stains on the bed are visible even in the heavy crimson mist. The curved metal flourishes of the bed frame, clothes on the floor, mossy water damage in dramatic pink strips, the door slightly ajar – were we that careless? Was I *really* unaware of that? I've been in that room a hundred times. I've rented that room just to toss off in, to have self-important drunken-girly-huffs and mid-session naps, to take photos of old women, proper ruins and really very revolting creatures, and in most of the other rooms in that hotel. Smile Guesthouse. Pod's true pathfinding was the dusty picture over the top of my half asleep, massage-oiled, topless handjobs from a university student covered in acne I used to take to the same rooms I'd made real crimes in earlier. Her tits were something – they were like old hard lumps of plasticine in ultra-sensitive watery skin, they were flap and lump and thick and I wasn't supposed to kiss and suck them but she always relented more square territories of skin as I got sleepier somehow. At five in the morning, cut in two by alcohol and half-dead, when I saw her lurking I'd get an erection so hard it was painful. The thought of her hands on me now is infinitely more powerful than the Fat Ladyboy, I'm so pleased and relieved and proud that I can know this – I've always privately defined myself through the flavours of my satisfaction in ugly handjobs.

The first time I met the Fat Ladyboy I procrastinated about going back to her apartment in spite of her invitation, in my caution I felt it was enough of an achievement at first to simply get her phone number and agreement to help me. The second and third times we went to sex hotels in the Klong and I directed her and took pictures, feeling extremely pleased with myself after and drinking heavily in celebration. The fourth time we went to her apartment early in the morning in a taxi and I admired the way she held herself in spite of my disgust. I was very struck by her bathroom which I visited before seeing the rest of the apartment; a chaos of make-up and feminine equipment, half-used, rotten single-use objects, vandalised, and collected in obsessive hermetic order into plastic boxes and trays when not strewn in arcs across the floor, like a drunken artist's studio, like an art installation, and the toilet bowl had shit stains in it and the room's air was rich, and the mirror was thick with coloured fingerprints and make-up smears. Now of course, in my simplistic pretension, I wish I'd taken photographs of that room, masturbated inside it, hidden things there. I wish I thought about it more. I could have put out a monthly journal about that room. Before I look at another worse toilet, I want to finish this paragraph by describing a final red photo of the Fat Ladyboy's head buried face-first in the bed sheet, arms out in front joined again at the elbows, hair in sad, wild cascades, body cut off under the shoulders by the photo's vertical edge. As I look through these now I am sliced through.

Here is one of a house that cuts its rent from your body. An alley of fresh shit leads into the settlement, opening into clusters of half-finished concrete shells, blown out and patched up with tarpaulin and chicken wire, clung to weakly by parasitic shacks of wood and corrugated iron. Observe the ashen ground, strewn with bricks and rubble and shit, flies, plastic bags and animal bones. The voluptuous stench of rotten fruit is the highest of all slum and jungle odours. Two old women sold us a slab of ice, beer and white liquor while a third crone, horribly obese, hacked a pile of entrails on a thick wooden block with a hatchet, her watery arm-fat swinging like a counterweight with each stroke. I wiped the sweat from my eyes to keep watching as we walked on. Between two great hunks of concrete was a plank leading over a stream of oily green water, making an island of a row of wooden huts on stilts. What a picture we had been on this happy night; four young, hard-drinking, hot-blooded com-panions kicking off our shoes and climbing a ladder of old bamboo into the first hut, the Love-Chateau of Naen and Ling.

Settle now in the Chateau, a baking womb of tenderness and friendship. We happy four reclined on mildewed blankets, cut ice and poured drinks into metal cups, lit cigarettes, turned on the karaoke machine, shed our sweaty rags and sank down into the special tainted moisture of the Chateau. All the pornography in the world is an under-tier to certain ancient smells. We all looked at Naen's cock and she held forth with stories about it; sometime ladyboy fuck ass man, sometime customer want suck me, understand? Yes, Naen loved sucking cock, and she was mildly embarrassed to tell us that when she beat herself off she thought only about licking and snuggling and sucking hard cocks. One time she raped a young western bi-curious customer and we all laugh. You can get away with anything in lipstick.

Shit and its odours are important elements of a slum and I looked forward to occupying the toilet in privacy and taking stock of the proceedings there. My legs ached as I pulled myself outside into the hot air and the blood rushed in protest to my head. The heat and light and smell of the place overwhelmed me and I let the cigarette fall from my lips with a vacant significance. I drowned happily in the churning intensity of the sky, the scratches and floaters in my eyes making it squirm with worms and plankton. A brightly coloured spirit-house outside could not subtract from the breathtaking glory of decay. The toilet was directly beneath the Chateau, a hole in the ground that connected with some plumbing somewhere so you could flush by pouring a bucket of water down into it. The toilet area was made private by woodgrain boarding nailed to the four stilts supporting the Chateau, sealing it completely in pitch black and glamorously amplifying the heat and stench inside. I'd been given a torch and told to watch my head as the ceiling, the floor of the Chateau, was only four feet from the ground. My brain reeled as I squatted and sweated and shat like a poodle into the nasty hole.

In this one the sun is rampant as we enter an unfinished, eight-storey concrete building with thick, high thresholds across every bare entrance, over some of which a species of ivy had crept. My sweat is a coating of pus sealing my body. Families of squatters occupy each series of empty concrete rooms, glaring and alert with hostility. In one room a lone crying infant is tied by the ankle to a breeze-block with a piece of wire. On the second floor Naen buys what we need from a fat woman nursing a baby in a room piled with dusty roofing tiles. Back on the street Pod and I are relieved and elated, and once again in our slum with the Chateau in sight I am positively euphoric. I go back to the old woman and buy more beer and ice, and some form of fried pastry-like confection that is soon forgotten. I prance like a child through the stones and the smells and delight washes through me in an invigorating wave.

The stuff cascades into my mind like shattering crystal and removes the alarm that would normally accompany the cramps and liver-stabs and lung-punctures. My life is perfect and my heart is full and with Pod at my side I am in a totality of harmony. With shivers of lust I looked at Ling, the wet wobbly she-man, and invited it to join me down in the toilet. I collected a sex-kit of the torch and a blanket and we crawl, bent over with desire, down into the darkness below. With the torch stood upright like a candle Ling made a ghastly toothy smile and pulled her knickers off from under her miniskirt to show me a glistening slug. I pulled one of her man-tits free from her top and groped it whilst I slithered free from my sweat-piss trousers. The tit felt like a smooth little purse of sinewy meat and the nipple was tiny, like a child's nipple. She leant over and put my cock in her mouth, kissing the head and then using a piston jack-hammer motion taking her lips right down to the hilt with every stroke. For ten minutes I was in a state of machinery, existing only in my cock, which was the only fixed point in the universe. I pictured my organ alone, erect and charged, a furious and beautiful mushroom, and held fast to the image in my mind as I stirred Ling's slippery glans and exploded in her mouth.

I felt I would faint if I got up, and my vision went out of focus when I opened my eyes. I find the sun reacts with a powerful sadness that I feel for the impermanence of corridors, labyrinths and stenches, the contrast of jungle-green against dusty concrete, illusory fellowship in courage and imagination, and I understand how important light is and how to use it. And always with this comes strange fatigue, an inertia that is just weak enough to trigger an instinctive resistance, which produces an ache that is so tender and subtle; I call this longing, and it is a species of rapture. And I also hold that the true heights of happiness in experience and understanding are anchored by an oppressive isolation in adulthood.

Here is the last from this cycle. The smoke from the rust had the flavour of sweet, burning plastic and it stripped my throat and lungs; I could taste the iron flavour of blood on my soft palate. Sometimes my heartbeat shook me like a boat engine, and the next minute fell away to nothing. Pod's naked body was the colour of beetroot and alive with a horrible, spasmodic shivering, each limb to a different tempo. An end must come to all good things, to all special things. In this moment, as I felt close to madness and death, ten members of Naen's family arrived at the Chateau after their nightshift, dressed in grey custodial uniforms and carrying between two of them Naen's father, an elderly cripple in a vest and chinos. I laughed and my eyes watered and bubbles of blood came into my mouth, my legs went into cramp and my eyes stung from poison sweat. I am given a piece of fermented fish which I cannot remember how to swallow once it's in my mouth, and it falls from the orifice like a turd from an anus. I am without faculty, and again feel something resembling contentment as I know there is no other choice or behaviour, there is nothing further, nothing other than romantic flashing images and automated endurance. This was a good thing, a valuable and special thing. Ling cradles my head tenderly on her chest and everyone takes a turn to pose with us for a photograph. I try to smile for the camera each time and am rewarded with vocal approval and some applause.

—Sometimes it speaks Thai, says Naen.

None of my photos are taken with knowledge of theory or technical proficiency or whatnot. As ever, I'm not an artist. I just want the proof that my visionary participation in human geography justifies the memories I labour under today. I want the proof that I was capable of cruelties I no longer celebrate so simplistically and recklessly. And I do labour, I'm trying to be constructive, I do actively want to take responsibility. I always try to sidestep what time does to this iconography, hoodwink it, put off the aspect of decline, and there's always less and less to work with. I have to do more with less.

I still can't drive myself to fully commit to some elements of my history; I write around them in flirtatious, self-important flourishes, making of them the buried heart of this text. I set up a series of websites primarily to sell my CDs, poorly assembled, and frantically, pretentiously named and renamed them, uploaded photographs and deleted them, worried about the photos, rearranged them, justified them, cropped them, captioned and un-captioned them, and made shy allusions to their narrative contexts that I imagined were of great consequence. In the end no one cares very much about the gay little details. Only my friends cared about my vicious attitudes and arrogance, the offensive flavours of which I never fully understood when they were under

the puritan examinations of tedious, Edinburgh prot-
estant scenes. Flat pints of cheap lager and coffee-table
experimentation. I thought I was doing what artists are
supposed to do. I really never ever was. I wasn't, in that
way, like them; I can't stop talking to that internally. I felt
a responsibility and a sense of commitment. To myself,
and what I'd done with my name.

My efforts to construct a Tropical Gothic are most
rewarded in the phenomena granted me by the Klong,
and I must handle the Klong with great care and tenderness, as I would the sallow, dangling breast of one
of its ugly whores. I photograph, write, fuck, and day-
dream on, over, through, with and alongside the Klong.
(I now think of the Klong as the direct inverse of this
mountain.)

I pull a series of screenshots from Google Street
View of the Klong. As much as possible I try to retain
the dreary composition that I favoured for the covers
of my CD releases, facing roads, alleys, canals, bridges – simple demonstrations of balanced depth perspective in red light areas. Sticking to this obvious template
and method, I review these screenshots with reference
to my taken photos of other holes. Once thirty or forty of the former are chosen and collected into a slideshow, I am without doubt that the screenshots really are
superior, much more satisfying. The uniform, simply
disciplined composition gives a pleasing structure of
variation and repetition, a looped tunnel, timeless, endless, full of sex. The road I have chosen runs along the
whore's side of the canal from which the Klong gets its
simple nickname. The canal is black and stagnant and
thick as oil. The air is foul. As the slideshow moves me
at random distances along the soi, the self-generating
scenery along the sides is distinguished not only by ge-
neric filth and decay, open-sided hovels and the naked
homeless, but by an abundance of trees and luminous

green foliage, weird gardens and derelict wooden mansions. And everywhere whores, young and old and all cheap, sit on plastic chairs facing the road, and Google has helpfully smeared out their faces, pulling my attention to the rude little mysteries from which the eye darts down systematically to the tit, and finally to the Google arrow-markers that point out the directions of my advance. It's so similar to what the real location offers. Right now, I will allow that this slideshow that I have made is of an equal pornographic value to the real location, and of a superior artistic value to any of my other slum-hooker photography.

So now, I splice in some shots of breasts in Klong hotel rooms randomly between the street perspectives. I want this place to be permanently indivisible from huge and abnormal breasts. The latter in terms of the holistic feeling and essence of drooped breasts that burns through and fertilises me into action, the *potential* of hanging breasts, butterballs, the power of that, the instantaneous reduction and total wash. Flush. And specifically, as follows, spliced into and between the Klong screenshots randomly, separately:

Spotlit damp flesh cut off at the neck. Lived-in hide, smoothed to marble stretch in heavy hang, the bulbous top – sunken shoulder back, arm fronds, hands removed by frame. But I remember the little claws, wrapping round it. Squeezed. Little squeezes. Chest-press swollen flat before orb roots at tricep – *fuck*. The hang of the spread. There it is. What's amazing here is pinched-thin, off-set steeple-nips on perfect spread, under relief of asymmetric skin-brown cup. Warm, lit, I remember, and the chassis – in some ways, those great open hips and soft wobble centre smooth, the *femininity* – though cut off again above button. Good. The usual smirching patches and wear, here and there as season, but rows of dark sucked circles from that Chinese compression cup.

I zoom in on the flop. There are three inflamed, torn
off whiteheads and a y-shaped red vein on the organ;
also the nipple has a white flake of skin I want now to
pull off. (I also *just* remember the wiry thatch, inner
thighs and tattoo. And I believe the first totally illiterate
person I ever paid for sex. She gave an easy gam but
kept stopping at intervals to tell me what I thought were
contrived third-world sob-stories designed to make me
sentimental, but once I started to get in she did it right
and I was fine. I came back again and again. I emailed
the pictures to a friend with her approval.)

Grassy trails between buildings, some parked pick-
ups, the corner of a wooden shack with a CD hanging
down from a piece of cat-gut.

Though a wee belly sullied by a butterfly tattoo, is
an hourglass, Penthouse piece. Though large, as it goes,
perfectly symmetrical breasts, nipples up high betray-
ing her young age. Not my thing. Politely dusky 1920s
shadowed crotch and quite beautiful hips and upper
thighs – cut off under there. Knickers in one hand,
long fingernails dangling from the other, and smiling a
charming toothy crooked smile for the camera. It's remarkable that these women's vaginas are inoffensive to
me in the photos somehow. But the pictures earn their
subjects my loyalty, and easy familiarity. I have extremely fond memories of all these people, besides the images
they've become.

The concrete wall coming from the east. There's a
crack, there's black exhaust fumes and a weed, and a bit
of rag.

Spotlit from the camera flash, head thrown back
behind collarbone and underside of chin, giant but re-
markably light breasts bloomed out there in the centre
of the image. Not watery, neither hard nor heavy. Small,
chewy bud-like nipples. I just disintegrate into myself
for this. And I can feel the leafy slum and the black canal

on either side of it. Nothing on Earth is more valuable to me. It's all utterly contained and curated, internal and external, happening to me forever right now, in this photograph which I duplicate and revere. I would have it out – I would have this elsewhere – I'd have some worthy vehicle serve it over new fields.

Unusually for Google, this manages to nail down the unforgettable scent of the black water and you can sense how it withers the low-hanging leaves, making them lilt with its impurities. You can almost see the slim steps that lead right down to the water in this image. Some people, including me if I'm sober, climb down a few steps to urinate into the filth. It's as if your piss is swallowed into some negative matter from which light cannot properly reflect. The surface barely ripples; it just absorbs the piss which is devalued into thin, flowery cordial as it falls casually out of the world.

I've had a dramatically mixed relationship with soi dogs. I've loved a few dearly and had fights with others that have been almost as physically and psychologically damaging, as intimate, as much of the human violence I've known. Once I watched a dog drown in the canal near that same staircase. A street fight had started between two groups of youths, half-naked, skinny and jacketed in tattoos, they ran amok and were mostly shouting and throwing bottles at each other across the canal. The dog must have been suddenly disturbed, I heard it slap into the gloop before I understood what was happening. As the youths melted away all attention turned to the animal, but no one wanted to risk getting the canal water on them. A spindly old man came over with a fruit cutter: a very long piece of bamboo with a blade attached to gather fruit from tall trees. He calmly arranged himself with all his weight leaned back over one leg and lowered the handle to the struggling animal's face so as to guide it by the mouth over to the steps.

It either didn't understand or had invested too much effort in trying to keep its wide eyes and muzzle above
the oil, and took about ten minutes to tire before being
swallowed under. The man just silently held this long
stick over it, people came and went, and we sat at our
table watching.

Pigment-disorder Pim. I don't know why she was
crying, why she was so into it, or what she was thinking about. I felt utterly shut outside of it. It started
whilst the light was still off. It wasn't anything to do
with me. I thought. About Roy. And his Cambodian
gam as he listened to someone screaming in the booth
beside. Is it all just learnt repetition? Is that why I took
these pictures? Am I fucking a man with my cock in
the mouth of a weeping whore and my hand in a camera? It ruins what I'm trying to do with this slideshow,
that you can see my cock in one of them, even if it is
buried in the big rubbery mouth of a crying girl with
hair all around. What should I have done? She ignored
me. I asked her what was wrong and she ignored me.
In such a way that I knew that she knew what she was
doing. I've felt this before, many times, with whores,
who express themselves onto you in some assertive
and firmly purposeful way. I was intimidated. I actually felt vulnerable being in that sexual situation and not
understanding something that was being deliberately
withheld from me, and at the same time, at that precise time, being all over me. There was real risk. That
is really what it was like. It would have been dangerously rude, it would have been not the correct thing
to *forcefully* stop her. For all I know very dangerous.
And it would have taken force, assertive physical effort,
I imagine. And lost in memory as I write this, I fool
myself I was already on the way to coming. But look at
the photos. That's simply not true. I took a great long
series of photos, in which the tears seem very clearly to

be the subject. Now. And I can only remember how my own adolescent vulnerability rationalised the situation. Time after time. In the Klong.

There's that dirty, spidery old table again. The best table. Wet with melted ice and the stalks and hard bits of nibbled raw vegetables and drowning ants, and some smears and pieces of dribbled sauce. Evoking the table in this way and looking at the internet's weird photographic record of it gives me that over-smoked feeling. I'd smoke neurotically from the moment I sat down at the table, throughout the meal and beyond. The table positioned me at an advantage. Smile Guesthouse just ahead on the corner, strategic vantage over the bridge and crossroads and the protective cover of the tall tree above. A shrivelled old male corpse sat down at the table with me and made noises about rice. What? Yeah, have some rice. No, do *you* like rice? Sticky rice? Yes, obviously. It triggered my automatic lecture about European dietary variance, during which the endless washes around me illuminated the corpse's intention. We could eat some sticky rice in my house he suggested. It's not far from here.

I followed the hunchback carefully to his house – over the bridge which I enjoyed crossing with him and along the wet street to that brittle little row of Chinese munchkin homes with miniature hedged gardens in front of them. His papery claws looked marvellous undoing the big eighteenth-century padlock on the door, and my face got very close to them as I leaned down to take off my shoes. I bowed my head to get inside – strong smell of piss and Asian must. A strip bulb hanging vertically from the corner zapped on. Room was small and ceiling low, walls covered with dusty antiques, masks and icons, sepia photographs in rotten frames and cracked plastic wallets like what they used to put your driving licence in when it was still paper.

He was on his knees and bothering my hard with his little field-mouse claws. I winced a bit as he took it out, and my conscious mind took a meandering survey of his collection. Nestled into Khmer statuettes of Hindu gods, shrivelled foetuses and such were some more unusual images, very old photographs of a man with an extreme facial deformity sitting cross-legged behind a pair of crossed swords, with jars of matter all around him. Looking down at the dead hair across his skull, I felt the man's dry gums on my cockhead as his jaw went quiver-bite on it for a moment. I smelt an acute rip of foreign halitosis. You can't rid yourself of these smell memories. My whole body sort of collectively sighed out a romantic exhalation, and at the same time my hard completely wilted and a merciful dark seep of urine loosed itself out over the man's chin. I left him where he was on the floor and went back outside. I took a bottle of water from a crate beside the shoe rack, cracked it open and poured it over my cock before tucking it away, and stepping with care out of the garden.

But back to that important table. I'd like to conclude the slideshow with a photograph I don't possess and barely remember in visual terms. It's from the Dr. Ikkaku Ochi collection, I saw it some twenty years ago in Edinburgh. It shows a young Japanese girl with hypertrophied breasts from around 1900. I can't say any more about it, and I won't go on. About photos anymore. But the non-visual memory of that picture exfoliates permanently over and throughout the Klong – that's all that was ever going on there. It's what I felt it was time to move away from.

Do you know *allium ursinum*? For me, the strong gar-licky scent of this plant will always be a powerful signifi-er of guilt and sexual shame. I used to cut down swathes of it with a long stick when it was in season and I en-joyed the powerful erections that always accompanied this activity. I suppose that everything I try to set down springs from the primitive but fecundating technolo-gies of masturbation we employed as children, which I think I have been working back towards throughout all my adult life. Those early pleasures, steeped in nostal-gia and secrecy, were irrigated by cultural imperatives, fertilised by societies of peers, and became like basic elements: the matter of cells that are invisible. In addi-tion, the rigours of boxed routines made all proceedings and every act a ritual that carried a meaning, and these meanings were functional or superficial in themselves but collected together to point in a direction, and the direction concluded in something adult and distant.

It will help me here to return, as much as possible, to the first weeks of wandering, and how they allowed me to recall and curate my years in the swamps and slums of the centre.

Climbing through what's left of the fence that demar-cates my landlady's property from the forest and moun-tain proper, I felt a vitality in my intention. Through the bamboo thickets and banana trees first, then up the steep ridge that forms one side of the irrigation reservoir. Only the *pluang* trees of advanced growth had endured through this season's fires, leaving few tendrils as climbing aids on the ashen slope. At the top one is finally enveloped by the ancient dipterocarp, and in one's fatigue, all sense of direction; the way back to the lodge, the reservoir, the brick factory, are subsumed and lost in the starkness of only *up* or *down*. Here the mountain's awesome capacity for deceit is exercised upon one not fluent in its language. Identical and replicating patterns of twisted trunks and creepers collude with the whispering suggestions of paths between the pillars and patches of light to affect a malignant and immersed sense of dislocation.

I don't know for how long I climbed, I doubt it was more than ten or fifteen minutes. A good place appeared to me in the form of a shallow mouth in the earth caused by a tree that had fallen and rotted years ago. In terms of physical comfort, security and aesthetics, the mouth was ideal in its neutrality. And now pay attention: I perched myself on the dusty lip of the mouth facing inwards, unfocused my vision and turned my mind towards the Dwarf. The visual essence of the Dwarf. My imagination squirmed at first, unwilling to be held in place, and the effort leeched sweat from my already wet body. I knew it would be difficult. Oddly the Dwarf's miraculous breasts were actually the last element to settle in place. First came the little arm-stubs, obscenely muscular, and the flattened quad ribcage and trunk. Her smooth ochre skin that seemed nourished by the warm red earth, that beautiful skin, that made the smooth pads of her simian cheekbones, that split to form the rubbery flower of her sensual mouth, and pulled itself taut across the empty space above her nostrils. And her beautiful eyes of obsidian, arranged on her face asymmetrically like twisted arrowheads, bottomless and hypnotic, suggesting the deft movement of fish through water.

The next day I took some rice with me. Once lost, I began a deliberate program of wandering and sitting randomly with my eyes closed. I climbed for longer than the day before, entering a new phase of the mountain with more light. The forest led me to a lush, sun-drenched clearing, a swamp of green ferns, free of bigger trees. I felt physically pulled to choose this place but of course it was too stimulating to concentrate. Not far from that fertile crater I saw some fragments of grass brick sealed in flat, baked mud. The forest canopy was so high above me, the tinted dome of space divided neatly by the towering straightness of thin black trunks. This cavernous architecture gave me an acute sense of my specific location in a pressurised green vastness. I laid down my bag and carefully took off my shirt, folding it on top of the bag. I pulled off my vest, removed my shoes and socks, then my trousers and finally my briefs, laying them over my shoes beside the pile of clothes. Naked, I knelt down on the mud and shut my eyes.

On the third day, with the same lump of uneaten rice in my satchel, I managed to successfully masturbate onto a small rock in the trench of a dried-up stream. It was a piece of sedimentary sandstone about the size and shape of a sheep's heart. I held it in my left hand and came on it standing up, then laid it sperm-side down on the earth. After this I fell unwillingly asleep for fifteen minutes or so. The journey home was the most arduous yet, I would guess that it took over three hours. I think I doubled back on myself many times and felt some really intense bursts of panic accompanied by a heightened impression of time passing very quickly. Eventually I came out into some cultivated land near the chili field monastery and was so exhausted I jumped on the pillion of a passing farmer who kindly took me all the way back to the lodge.

On the fourth day as I began my ascent I had a strong urge to return to the scene of the crime and examine what was left of my sperm, but I knew even if I gave in to this urge I'd never be able to find the location. I tried to keep my eyesight unfocused and trained on the ground directly in front of me as I entered a dense maze of fig trees. Before I had even considered stopping anywhere the Dwarf entered my mind like a waft of opium, potent, still and as clear as the rays of the sun on running water. I began automatically to circumambulate the broad trunk of a towering hemi-epiphytic fig tree. When I tried to use my voice on a whim I was struck dumb by the majesty of my own concentration, for which I felt a new respect, as a dog senses the divinity of its master.

I walked slowly away from the fig tree and on through the bush, letting my unfocused gaze hover over the ground in front of me. I knelt and scooped up a handful of earth with my left hand and took out my erection with my right. I came like a plant, efficiently, without much effort or feeling, onto the handful of earth, and mixed the globules of semen into it with the drooping tip of my penis. Raising the mixture to my face I breathed it in sharply and then ate a small mouthful. The sensation of the earth in my throat was just awful.

Down there, outside of the forest there is only the institution of the city and the night. The men there recognise a hierarchy that I have now decided is illegitimate. A biography of the city would weave my history into that hierarchy for specific periods of time, and within those time-periods would be specific acts of mine, located along an arc. An ethnography of the night would record my background and progress, the documentaries I watched and the books I read, the men and women I selected to fuck and socialise with, and immortalise my sickly, narcissistic philosophies across its pages in Times New Roman. And these would rightly appear irresponsible and pathetic, as they mixed with the insipid swill of other misdeeds and formed veins of sewage across these Asian landscapes that I wish I could freeze out of time.

I'm not sure if it's the coffee in the morning or the beer and whisky in the evening that has weakened my bladder. I don't drink as much here on the mountain as I used to in Bangkok, and since my most liberated year there I've never pissed my bed at night again thankfully. But I do dribble after a normal piss, sometimes whole squirts down the inside of my trousers, especially when I'm shaking from nicotine and coffee anxiety. A few times up on the mountain I pissed in my trousers intentionally, for convenience and as a misguided experiment. I had to lie down flat against the earth again to relax enough to let it out, and even then it came in unsteady spurts. I couldn't walk and piss at the same time like I wanted to. Sometimes, down there in the bars in town, drinking with fat, old, unwashed men, I'd think pissing myself a bit was an appropriately nostalgic thing to do, along with chain-smoking and matching every beer with liquor. I would sometimes leave the bars very depressed by the men and swear to myself that the next day I would just disappear from them for good. Drink at another bar, another soi, another ket, drink at home, not drink. Be on the mountain. But, disgustingly, it was the men I went to the bar to be with in the first place, not the girls, and I always went back, and I always kissed the men's sweaty jowls, and drank into long lines of credit, and was among the last to leave, riding my roulette machine full-throttle over the empty roads and stopping by the canal in the same fucking puddle to buy a plastic bag of flat noodles in pig's blood to eat in bed before the night's last throat-hacking smoke as I pissed through the slats on my veranda.

I've never shat myself I don't think, as a result of deliberately negligent behaviour. A hooker I once took
home in Bangkok shat herself quite badly I recall, as a
result of her exertions in a vomiting fit in a taxi after
two bottles of cheap red wine from some Arab hole that
I warned her not to drink. Back at my room she went
unconscious and I peeled off her clothes and dragged
her into the bathroom to hose her down. When I pulled
off her black knickers, I was so disbelieving that it was
actually real shit in them I was looking at that I raised
the mess up to my nose to smell. It was odourless, like
my piss-yellowed sheets. I could have rolled it into pel-
lets and put them away in drawers. I also took photos
of the mess and the woman, who didn't wake up until
morning. I've shat outside quite a few times as an adult,
several times on the mountain. I must say I don't much
care for it, I far prefer wetting myself as long as I am
alone.

That dribble of piss is starting to become a permanent constituent of my personality. A belligerent, mildly
obnoxious streak that seeps through, an excuse, a defence. I grimace under it every time I turn from the
trough, fuck's sake, a tiny character-forming hardship I
must endure, a scar, a wrinkle, a limp, bad chest, swollen fingers. It's a part of what being a member here in-
volves, have you ever abandoned your family? Spent
time in prison? Fucked a child? Sucked off a ladyboy?
Pissed and shat in your trousers in public?

What depresses me most about the old men is their
lack of imagination. Dulled, pickled lobes, like drugged
fish in a tank or a marine farm. Making them like you
isn't difficult. You should see them in the daytime on
the rare occasion they emerge, shivering, sallow and
drenched in pungent sweat. Faces of total capitulation
and despair, being attended to, nursed like stroke victims. They continue like this through the years until

they stop eating, little by little, drink less and less, and are snuffed out in their rooms, alone in the bake. There are colonies of them in every province, even up here in the north. European and American bags of shit. Smelly old men, who do violence poorly, Luddites,that I feel resentfully attached to. Young men stay in Bangkok and the south. I watch myself around thuggish, cruel young men and it keeps me just a little bit humble, the fear of violence, but a great deal more depressed. And violence is a lot easier in Bangkok, and consequentially a lot more severe. But here, the old men leech a different form of hubris out of me. And that is why there is a political dimension to that dribble of piss.

Ten years ago I really wasn't trying to be or do anything specifically. The purity of those first few years was certainly the most contented period of my life. To have that kind of purity you can't have any notion of ownership. So unfortunately learning of any kind will corrode it, and that corrosive process gathers momentum quickly.

I've tried hard not to take notice of my naked body when I wash myself outside the lodge. I don't mind my cock, in fact sometimes I quite like it, but my anus disgusts me. Years of shitting parasitic, liquid rust must have stained my buttocks yellow, brown and red; that is how I imagine them, a chaos of primary colours. Tropical sweat rash has lacerated every fold in and around my groin and left my inner thighs and buttocks purple and skinless. Especially around my arsehole it feels like there isn't any normal skin, just wiry curls of sharp hair over packed blood and layers of dead skin. Every time I shit it soaks billions of spores into the mess. I can smell the iron of coagulated blood and shit just thinking about it. I see my face every day in the small mirror I have in the lodge, and of course I have little sense of it ageing. And now it's covered by my

snotty beard and moustache. But my groin and arsehole age shockingly because I don't look at them at all
often.

For the last few years here, my anus has punished me
with unpredictable bouts of maddening itchiness and
painful spasms. I wake in the night sometimes with my
finger jammed up it, either through or around my boxer shorts or sarong, and the disappointment and frustration of having to stagger outside to wash my hands
and discard the garments reminds me of when I used
to regularly piss the bed in Bangkok. Keen to believe it
was only sweat that had soaked the sheets, I'd hungrily
sniff the bed for verification, and find myself unable to
smell anything at all, except the cigarette I would smoke
to settle myself for sleep again. The spasm is like having
one's rectum stretched. It lasts about five minutes and
is totally incapacitating for that period. I simply fall to
the floor in a ball and clench my jaw with my eyes shut.
The itch, especially at night, is like ants running in and
out of your arse. Between the two it is the least agree-
able and the most frequent and depressing. Obviously it
has occurred to me that the origin may be in yet another hideous Asian parasite of some form, but I've strip-
washed my body raw with antibiotics more times than I
can remember since these symptoms first appeared with
no positive result.

When I was a child I would occasionally work my
arse with a Bic pen, sometimes with a condom over
it out of some awkward hygienic consideration. Then
when I realised the orifice was hardier than I'd pre-
sumed I started using cigar tubes, still with condoms
so I didn't need to lubricate with anything other than
saliva. Cigar tubes were conveniently sized and disposable. I never used my finger unless I was in the shower, and even then, I had little interest then, as now, as
to what the walls of my shit-tube felt like, much less

looked like. As a teenager, William Burroughs' faggot descriptions of pink, quivering male anuses appalled me.

My anus now feels like a distended ring of alien muscle, like a tough squid ring, with a number of rather worrying lumps in and around the flesh it's sewn into that itch especially acute. I'm grateful I don't enjoy getting reamed up it, imagine what it might look and feel like now if that was the case.

During puberty my nipples became sore and tender and swollen with what felt like a little ball-bearing in each. They changed shape, became more pink and then finally a mature purple brown, as the last female blossoms drooped and fell from my body. I haven't bothered looking at them for years now that they are covered with hair. I don't like other people sucking or pinching my nipples, but I'll pinch them myself through the hair when I pretend to be a woman.

On the mountain I've become less squeamish about my nudity and my body in general. It looks very different to me in this context. It's not like an animal's body, it doesn't make me feel like an animal at all. It couldn't be more human, it couldn't make me more aware of humanity. I've started to engage in forest-nudity not to become like an animal, not to participate in any kind of non-participation, not to make a sign for myself, or a popper. Actually it's a very human reason, a very sober reason. The material of my farming trousers rubs against my cock and I become aroused involuntarily. I was trying to work against that, so I remove my clothing and that problem is dealt with.

I also find that the higher I go, the longer I am gone, the less I feel like smoking. The purpose of smoking up there now is almost purely celebratory, undertaken after meaningful and decisive action, with self-satisfaction. One exception is the stress of decision-making and unusual situations. Normally my senses guide me effortlessly, without any conscious calculation, through the endless growth with the illusion of perfect randomness. The path of least security is not necessarily the most desirable; I'm not trying to master fear, it could be said that I am trying to reach maturity. In this context, I define maturity as consciously realised knowledge of myself. When conscious calculation interrupts this process at the level of decision-making, smoking can be undertaken in short sessions as a form of augury. Down underneath my tongue against the gummed wall of my inner jaw, set at the roots of my tongue, are two wormy ridges of mottled flesh, like some element of female anatomy, like the walls of a vagina, bumpy and lubricated and tensed. I feel tobacco special in these bumps. Like batteries of muscle that ache and spasm with overuse. When I smoke my pipe I trap the richest sweetest smoke in a bubble under my tongue to feast these ridges, and nicotine throbs through my brain like it's a slab of electrified meat-jelly.

Spitting is a revolting habit that I've had for as long as I've smoked, since I was eleven. I spit all the time, but especially when I'm smoking it's just impossible not to. I don't even notice I'm doing it. A few years after I started smoking a friend pointed out to me that I never spat when I was around a girl I liked in spite of the fact that I chain smoked. I hadn't thought about it and was furious that he mentioned this in front of the girl. I spit both saliva and phlegm, though I like to chew phlegm and play with it in my mouth first unless it's watery. I don't hack it up from my throat, and I'm not ostentatious in my spitting unless I want to signal my nonchalant disrespect for another man. Saliva is either messily sprayed out as fast as possible by collecting it on the end of my tongue and blowing it out between the tongue and teeth and upper lip, or letting it drool out in a slimy teardrop and fall loose with a rapid flick of my head.

Recently, I can't remember when this started, the taste of my mouth has become rank. When I catch a waft of my breath it's eye-watering, especially when I wake in the morning of course but throughout the day at large. Is it age, or too much coffee or my strict habit of smoking after I brush my teeth at night? It's increased my spitting too, and made me very cautious about getting close to people. I used to stagger into brothels and chemists and restaurants in the bright light of the morning and practice charming conversational flour-ishes with people in service without a second thought. And I would kiss hookers if the situation allowed or de-manded it, and kiss women whom I wasn't paying also. One morning in the old neighborhood, having drunk through the night and falling around with other tramps and stop-outs, I persuaded some American tourist into bed halfway through her breakfast. Back in her hotel room I sucked down all her opium through her little pipe and kissed her enthusiastically while I played with her fake tits. I was in no way inhibited when she told me that I smelt like a brewery, and she didn't physically communicate disgust. I slobbered on her rigid plastic nips and jacked off on her stomach while she talked shit, then left for home after lying that I was going out for cigarettes and condoms. Now, my mouth is smaller than ever, my lips are dry and puckered and hidden in a beard and moustache. When I smile it cracks open like a sharp crescent moon and reveals my squint yellow teeth, pointing inwards. I won't face society of any kind unless I have mint gum or more often these days dried thyme to chew or stuff under my lip in a wad, like a quid of tobacco. It's the only way I can stand to swallow my own saliva.

In moving north to the mountain, I am leaving not just the city and the night as a flipbook of images, but that fraternity of brothers and uncles that operated its own synergy of meanings: the institution of the sodality of Cambodia.

The first time I saw Uncle Martin, in a wooden guesthouse on the lake in central Phnom Penh, he was dressed in a torn t-shirt and a pair of trousers tied with string, blocking my view of the television at nine in the morning, belching and farting simultaneously like a farm animal, a half-lit Pall Mall in his mouth as he peered at a DVD cover and scratched himself – what a revolting display I thought, what an absolutely base and repugnant specimen. I told him in explicit terms about this days later as he, Pod and I sat inebriated round a card table, where we'd been gambling straight for twelve hours, and we laughed so hard he vomited mouthfuls of blood all over the floor which were duly set upon by trains of ants and clouds of flies the colour of topaz. Uncle Martin was a smoker of genius, a refined drinker of spirits, and in those last months, an abstainer from solid food. His body, the most withered and abject leather envelope, emitted a variety of strikingly unique and different perfumes of illness as he began dying, and I breathed them in deep out of curiosity and friendship as the three of us drank, gambled and acted towards his promises, in a succession of progressively beautiful campaigns. His room smelt like a mixture of urine and coriander when Pod, a policeman and I gently lifted his corpse out of it, and in doing so felt as though we were robbing a mausoleum. Even the heartless cop was struck with the impression of desecration – it was written deeply into the lines of his grimace.

Uncle Martin's sugary laughter and glints of gentility could not cover his scars or tattoos, nor the distant brutality in his smiles. He had used his gotten gains to erect the concrete skeleton of a residential building somewhere in the Philippines, a country that he painted as a sort of paradise that balanced the hell of Cambodia. We knew he could not ever return there, and it was more a colourful narrative tool in his sermonising and laments than a real subject of mundane intention. (All of us respected the pretence that Cambodia somehow held us captive.) Pod was my closest friend and my passion both before and after Uncle Martin and others like him, and I've come to think of us now as Charles Ryder and Sebastian Flyte in *Brideshead Revisited*.

Leben Der Heiligen:
Or, Some Historical Notes on Pod

Pod's consumption of beer has now become a much stranger discipline, practiced with the most fragrant tragedy of faith. What were previously casual tastes and preferences, habits and characteristics, have become a codified ritual etiquette and body of precepts. Whereas beer was an important social and sexual tonic that gave structure to the performance of deeds, it is now the end itself, with both sex and society of every kind made subservient to it. They both are absent from the trinity now, which has solidified into one monolithic value that prohibits movement, rather than facilitating it. As such, in its apotheosis, the volume of beer consumed has increased, but unlike other drinkers, Pod's consumption is highly regulated with attitudes, conditions and a general monastic rigour and outward absence of joy.

He awakes in the hours that follow noon and primes himself with caffeine and rice-gruel. In these first hours, it takes him great efforts of concentration to control his shaking convulsions and violent bowel eruptions. Following this primer, he engages in several hours of punishing physical exercise, at any physical cost and regardless of location. The regimen is again joyless and stark, designed for the practice of endurance in contained spaces, such as prison cells, small hotel rooms and the hovels of slums. It is manifest in the taut and brutal physique that is Pod's primary attribute. Tarnished with quickened age and poisons, the red skin is stretched over rippling muscle like a diving-suit, his shaved head an angular helmet, his poise like a scorpion's, bearing the heavy weapons of his limbs gracefully, without effort.

He will not begin drinking beer even a minute before the sixth hour, and neither convenience, temptation nor boredoms of any nature can see this observance broken. When it begins, he will not raise or touch glasses, nor toast or make social exclamations, as he is absorbed in the privacy of his relationship with the beer, a communion that would be compromised by any foreign, external etiquette.

He drinks the cheapest beers available and heavily dilutes each glass with ice. He drinks quickly, but with the illusion of his barely touching the glass, and when in his company, one would attest to seeing him only refill a half-drained glass with ice but never drink from it. It is a deeply refined and mysterious form of consumption. Routinely, Pod drinks between two and three bottles as I drink one, and urinates with much, much less frequency.

(On Phnom Hill, five swarthy men play a pounding, fluid polyphony on xylophones and bells in a crumbling, open-sided pavilion. It is revelatory, ecstatic, and I submit to it with the deepest humility. Pod is offended by the gift's license, and sees a wantonness in my submission that makes me resent him very deeply for several moments, as the Chevalier hates and fears the peasant.)

Pod is one of the great smokers. Though able and willing to enjoy the dark, sweet, rubbed tobaccos I favour, Pod smokes the cheapest, lowest quality local cigarettes, at the rate of two packs a day. These cigarettes unwrap and disintegrate before one nears the filter, which itself absorbs and retains an unusual degree of heat that sears the lips and fingers. The tobacco in these cigarettes is desiccated and stalk-ridden, its smoke caustic and sour like burning plastic. So profound is its odour, so suggestive of physical harm to lesser men and smokers, that the Olympian genius of Pod's smoking is alight like a powerful beacon. I found the sweetest poetry in his friendship and his smoking.

His room and its surrounds are replete with ashtrays of acrid waste, his thumb and two forefingers are stained with dark nicotine-yellow, his skin is dusted with sour-smelling ash, his undressed cot fragrant with it, the whites of his deep-set eyes are orange and refined with the sallowness of brilliantly advanced smoking, his saliva is coloured and pungent, and he hacks great yields of loose, heroic phlegm from his raw trachea and spews them like a charmed fertilisation upon the Cambodian soil, over which we roamed together in many worthy directions.

As his decline and collapse give shape to what I have now become, the nature of religious tissue is revealed: undifferentiated, malleable, a primary matter to be harnessed and given form by great men like Martin. This reproductive process of cultural patronage transformed the physical matter of Martin's body. (In this country, old men accumulate followings around themselves, who collect and curate the physical waste from their bodies as powerful treasure: their betel spit, urine, turds and nail-clippings. In time, and especially after death, these relics turn to crystal and spontaneously divide.)

Pod and I not only tolerated, but derived a curious pleasure from washing Martin's exhausted body and laying it down carefully on his cot. This usually occurred in the brightest hours of the morning when commands are received from an unconscious layer of the mind that has started to dream in desperation. We would fold his leathery wings behind him in silence, and with a tender but clinical precision that the tiled grid of the communal shower-room dictated. The room was respected by all the guests as an antechamber for Martin, despite the hatred and disgust in which he was held by some other long-term residents. His life and deeds were possessed of a palpable gravitas written in his aura; assertive, coherent and thoroughly consistent; leaving the flowers of his authority growing everywhere throughout the wooden corridors, and the very wood itself seemed marinated in his urine. The showerhead spurted water in very fine jets at uneven angles, which created an impression of the room slowly filling with moisture like a tepid sauna. Martin's skin would become damp, and then cursed with a froth of creamy soap that Pod and I had rubbed into him, and which fell away like scales with the water we poured over his body with plastic spoons from the trough. I was especially gentle and respectful with the papery skin that covered his thighs, and the wooden, vegetable quality of his kneecaps that put itself in evidence when we bore him up and down to his cell. When Martin is dead, I thought, we'll roll dice made from his kneecaps.

In addition to his very memorable hide (ripened ochre by the same Philippine sun that smiled on underworld punishment flayings on a mountain outside Olongapo), Martin's primary attribute is the lumpy, scarlet blood that he coughed up with each of the sixty Pall Mall that he smoked in a day. He howled through his coughing like a mongrel and his movements took on the involuntary character of a vomiting child: disturbingly agile gestures of physical distress. His arms would fold back like a dog's ears and quiver as he retched. His face and clothes were often stained with blood, and blood-soaked tissues and rags surrounded him everywhere and always. This loud, gory and highly intrusive spectacle of his attempts to smoke full cigarettes at five or six minute intervals dominated the hotel's lakeside restaurant where we spent most days and nights. Uncle Martin had lived in the hotel longer than any other long-term guest, and the staff had long since learnt how to accommodate his needs and behaviour. He was generous and polite with them, and the sacredness, the *hierophany,* of his long, bloody death and its constant rituals was politely facilitated and ignored as required. Martin was not really human to the Khmers, and they were like Apsara to him – he would watch them sometimes with bright eyes and a delighted smile, like a Victorian mill-owner watching fairies at the bottom of his garden.

Life on the lake was structured by one long card game. Pod, Martin and I sat at a special round card table on the jetty, partially enclosed by wooden latticework and hanging plants that formed a booth-like grotto, a private chapel of gambling. The grotto stood alone over the water with a short connecting walkway, making it convenient for Martin's lung complaints – he could spit and vomit into the water through the relative integrity of the hanging flowers without standing up. The grotto raged with the sounds of laughter and vomit. At this table, membership was granted through a fetish for tropical discomforts. Martin was unquestionably senior and more ritually pure and experienced than Pod or I. In such a relationship, repeated exclamations and advice from the senior entity are delivered down as slogans and maxims. Pod and I operated under the treasured sword of *Sinit mangone ad periculum accipere*, a rubric that became sacred and indivisible from the experience of Uncle Martin. We novices took a regular, extended interval during the day to sleep, whereas Martin had no established pattern of rest. If he tired, we'd support either side of his weak gait back to his cell or the shower-room, and he would reappear after no more than a few hours, all bright-eyed and blood-spattered leather, under a quite glorious halo of funereal musk. I could hardly contain the happiness and excitement I felt to see him again.

Let me now gather together an image with all these attributes, and balance them in this system of values by which we operated. Martin was the sun disappearing behind the peak of a mountain; his bleeding and noise was the drama of ritual sacrifice. Anthropologists and mystics know the potent religious opportunities contained in all forms of liminality – waking dreams before sleep, forested swamps between countries, the period between day and night in which bodies of water, trees and buildings are suddenly recast in limpid and mysterious colours. Martin himself in his long death was also that liminality: he was sacred. Wherever he moved, he was located at the centre of a cosmology of rose petals, represented perfectly by tissues stained with his blood. At the outer limits of this cosmology were two, lithe Khmer hookers who physically joined with him at the end and the beginning of some terrible, degenerative cycle. Unable to remove myself, I pressed my face into the bars covering his unglazed window as he lay across his cot. The hookers stood either side of him in their perfect equanimity, with the grace and stylised gestures of Apsara dancers. Arms outstretched in a symmetrical tableaux, they stroked the filthy, bent twig of his cock in unison, teasing it out of its moleskin hood, and the room became filled with his strange, sweet farts.

When the Annamites of Dong Son wished to deactivate the power of sacred drums, they would ritually bore holes through the skins of the bronze instruments and deposit them on mountains. I am engaged in that process now. The best tool for the job is the heightened memory of cruelty. Now more than ever my heart is filled with hatred, which I will bring to bear upon myself in forests of revenge.

Shortly before his death, Pod and I removed Martin from the hotel for an outing to the brothels of Street 104. We sat in a dark, loud bar with an exotic name surrounded by a score of young whores in cheap identical brassieres. I engaged a chesty girl who carefully wiped some of Martin's blood from my neck with a pink tissue, which she set gingerly on top of an empty Anchor beer tin. I stroked her thighs under the table as I ogled her cleavage. Pod disappeared in a plume of blue tobacco smoke with a Vietnamese girl. Martin sat bandy-legged in a grotto of human flesh throwing playing cards down on the table, his chin wet with coke. The coke tin, which was coming to replace his usual rum drink as he was eating less, suddenly became the centre of the room as a light reflected across it. It caused me to feel a strange flutter of loneliness. I drew heavily on my cigarette with no pleasure. I asked my girl for a whisky and the bill. She brought these and then we left together, back to the lake in a tuk-tuk. I imagined Martin's image sealed in plastic, hanging from the rearview mirror.

Drunk in the tuk-tuk, I couldn't wait to get her big breasts out of the brassiere. My hard ached as I imagined the shower-cooled soft flesh and the big, chewed nipples and broad areola I wanted her to have. I wanted to feel the wobbling weight of her breasts on my thighs as she wanked me into her mouth in a prolonged and sustained effort, with the head of my cock inside her mouth. I didn't want to assert myself, I didn't want to move or even slightly fuck or pump into her mouth, I didn't want to nuzzle and suck nipples like I normally live for, curled up like a baby. I'd have sucked my own cock in her presence if I could. I didn't want to worry about her. I wanted to look at and feel her tits on my balls and thighs. No kissing or squeezing and cuddling – that aggressive hand and full-body squeezing that sometimes happens with prostitutes, when they are so depressed and hostile and you are craven and lonely and cynical, but there is some base resonating hum of vulnerable empathy somehow, and you find yourselves suddenly wrapped up together tightly in tears and ribbons and flowers. No desperate sympathy. Just the sustained effort of her mouth and her banging, slapping, heavy breasts.

Actually I don't want her little hand, even though my dick becomes even more packed tight at the thought of the ribbed rubbing effect of her fingers running up and down, but that's not how I want to come. I want just her mouth going up and down, as smooth and regular as a hydraulic pump, I want just that one dedicated rib of her lips gripping and rubbing my whole tubular penis from head to hilt, and as the lips slide back up from the hilt to the head, her tongue lolloping around my piss-hole and the barnacled rim of my helmet. That's how I'm going to come, and I want it emphasised by the position of her hands, safely down and away. This is prostitution. The experience, knowledge and confidence to extract satisfaction from a scenario loaded very much against you, like when you buy a new, nicely bound book, or when a painting is framed and hung, or a stool is kicked away underneath some cunt, or when some fucking cunt has his brains bashed in with a hammer and then the whole thing is wrapped up and sealed forever. I preferred to take total responsibility, and that's what defined the practice for me in the first place. This is always the case, the more years, the broader the focus, you get older and you develop a greater respect for your environment, and at the same time a more ambiguous and tired imagining of yourself, or anyone. Sex, like religion and drinking and smoking, is tied profoundly to ideas about *place*. Sick animals who move to Asia for sex graduate at their own pace through a succession of categories and locations, with a very defensive certainty as to their current, particular category and location. There is cruelty in it from wherever you stand, I absolutely believe that.

In my room, she removed her top as I gurned like a queer and fingered my tool. I was draped across my cot and hadn't yet showered. (Unlike Martin and Pod, my cell had a bathroom attached – they were both true monastics whereas I was only a prince, temporarily ordained to further my political career.) As she removed the brassiere, the ripe, lush expanse of her breasts that had formed the basis of my planning simply fell away to nothing – I had been tricked, as in when a fishwife uses a syringe to inject small fish with water to make them look fat. The girl smiled and went into the bathroom to have a shower like nothing had happened, like no deception had been committed. Horrified, I followed her in.

We washed each other with the slim, white bar of soap, and she may have taken a hit of something before we presented ourselves back on the bed. I asked her for a blowjob and she laughed in embarrassment – she had never given one before and had no idea what she was doing. I spread out and guided her head quickly down to my thighs. I wanked myself furiously against her cheek and mouth while she giggled awkwardly. I was suddenly very taken with this new and unusual thing that was happening, and without warning shot cum tenderly all over her chin. Writing this down now, I cannot remember her face or her useless chest, only her dripping and desecrated chin.

Tuol Kok has been destroyed. One day all of Asia's fishbowls, red-light slums, hostess bars and entertainment zones and the hundreds and thousands and millions of whores in them will be lost. They'll be swept away in vulgar brushstrokes of development in the face of global organisations. I will never be a soldier with a soldier's social excuses, or a colonist, I'll never smell a world without plastic, other than the last whiffs left from childhood institutions that linger in my heart as relics of my false ideal, but, I am and have lived in the world of poverty and whores. Let me again gather together these elements into a single image, that will, whilst appearing insincere, communicate a much greater truth about the institution:

In the red light district around Street 51, Pod and I had gotten extremely drunk by drinking large, reckless glasses of straight whisky with our beer. I had submitted to the darkness and my spinning hallucinations. A young, enthusiastic Viet hooker with bright red lips called my name from behind me. I remembered her, I'd been upstairs with her before in this very place. Pod made grumbling, envious noises through his saliva as I followed the girl upstairs again, uselessly clutching my book in my right hand as a talisman. I remember triangle shapes in the wood as I paid for the key to a room for thirty minutes. After, she called my name from the bathroom. I put my cigarette in the bedside ashtray and walked into the bathroom, where I found her doing a show-off, stand-up piss into the toilet with a bright, slightly guilty smile on her face. She looked like a fountain cherub, groin pushed out in alluring stillness with a perfect arc of yellow urine flowing into the toilet bowl from the bump of her cunt.

Downstairs, the darkness on the street was ominously dense and complete, isolating the few wooden tables on the filthy road from absolutely anything else. In place of the usual cacophony of bar music, only a monolithic drone rang out like an ancient bell through the density. My sarong held up with my left hand, I held my book in the right, a smoking cigarette clasped in my lips. I saw that in order to continue drinking, Pod had had his hands nailed to the course, wooden table by a tuk-tuk driver. Little rivulets of his blood leaked out to each side. With his head arched right back, mouth open, Adam's apple like the head of an arrow about to emerge from his neck – his dusty, pockmarked skin and the sinewy musculature it contained looked stretched to its limits with the contortion of his position. His ragged wife-beater clung to his trunk, translucent with fluids. Two hookers Pod had obviously been talking to were swooning in the arms of the tuk-tuk driver to one side of the spectacle. A second driver was carefully and tenderly pouring liquid from a dark bottle into Pod's stretched, gaping mouth, taking deliberate care not to choke him and waste the product. I, for my part, and in my own way, simply made delicate little licks at the corners of Pod's eyes, from which bled slim ribbons of yellowish liquid potent with alcohol. I did this both as a gesture of support and respect, and I cannot deny, selfishly, as a means of economy – for that way I did not need to order another drink myself. I also was mindful of demonstrating my close and familiar alliance with Pod, whose predicament was quite beyond, was perhaps the ultimate, the final spectacle. A disgusting, bloated rat scuttled out of the gutter towards Pod. It was so arrogant and fat and slow, I thought nothing of stepping on its head immediately, which crunched like a rotten walnut under my sandal. Its thick, infected blood seeped out like a halo around its ruined head. Martin was dead, but he hung throughout this scene like the air itself. Pod's hands were like dead spiders, fingers curled around the nails in visual screams of pain. I cocked my bearded head to look under the roughly hewn wooden table – Pod's feet were held in place by a single nail, gore oozing from its point of entry. I pointed to Pod, with whom I was deeply in love, and said to the assembly in Khmer—

—He will grow greater as I shrivel and fragment.

I lower myself gently into exquisite discomfort when I look at the details and peculiarities of my own body through the eyes of women I've fucked. I can't have women suck my cock now. It's far too complicated, and complicating. I don't like to smoke cigarettes in hotel rooms anymore, even after I've come. I lie curled up on my side sweating, anxious, the effort of showering and leaving the room hanging over me like a day at work, trying to think through how I will bid the woman good-night and good luck. What specific words I should use. Look at her stuff folded there, handbag on top of high heels and bra, and her mobile phone with a sort of key-ring thing. It's an incredible, draining effort to face it. But I must.

There is nothing a prostitute finds more repugnant than a penniless, dribbling crybaby who just wants to cuddle. I've never been one of these weak creeps. Even worse, one who insists on affecting sympathy as a distraction from his own shabby circumstances, as if she is automatically lower and more base and worse off than he is, like a homeless or a refugee. Just watch her stiffen and shudder, look at the real disgust in that grimace as it deepens and widens into a sour sneer. Do you know what it feels like to have sex with someone who disgusts you?

I know what my dead-for-hours sperm smells like mixed with dried, ripe saliva on a woman's breasts. Between them. Breasts that smell of my filth. Brackish drips of sweat and smears of lipstick, tiredness, the impression of a professional lie. I'll have that precise, mixed texture of feeling and odour in my system, I'll ask to bring and place that here in the forest. These feelings and smells hang like drapes between the trees, forming private cubicles, whispering together as sound turns into light and the face of the mountain twists and turns inward. I am doing the right thing.

My early imaginings of the sexualised female form were as buxom Barbie-dolls, large breasts with no nipples and no vagina. *Usborne Children's World History* had very stimulating illustrations of buxom cavewomen, Egyptians and other ancients with full, nipple-less breasts in nonsexual, everyday contexts. Also voluptuous men with swords and piles of decapitated heads, men with figures like the follower of Bacchus who grapples with a snake in Titian's *Bacchus and Ariadne*. I used to get such a powerful hard-on when I imagined that the snake was actually thick rope or cord restraining the supple and terribly muscular nude form, and as ever, I would be the subject, the fastener of the rope and the passive spectator all at once, a problem that makes adult masturbation very difficult.

In Bangkok and other ideas, I moved from slum to slum, looking for not necessarily the most abject pictures. I lived in reveries that spun days of glorious inactivity, initiated from the briefest eye contact with some scowling, breasted ape. The most fleeting of glances. A flutter of sadness on the face of an old man, he was a soldier, his daughters are prostitutes. Fat and old women. Cruelty, I hoped, was everywhere and I simply felt so associated and close to it, it didn't occur to me to well-temper my ratted sensibility with boring questions about myself. Questions about the curves of their dog-black eyes, the glamour and prestige of rotten mouths and stained teeth, the small bulge of sweaty tit on your smelly, grumpy Chinese aunt. My slum years have left me with an interest and appreciation for lengths of cloth and textiles, and all-purpose tools. You simply have no conception of how useful, how indispensable, a good length of quality cloth is.

At my most socially engaged, I embarked on explor-atory strolls that rarely lasted a half-hour in the debili-tating heat that I wasn't at that time even nearly used to. The climax to these was the sight of some fatty's naked breasts in the doorway of a hovel, or a younger woman breastfeeding, to which I would swoon and explode in-ternally, drenched with nervous tobacco lust and aban-don, and often come in my trousers spontaneously, do you believe that? I barely can now, but it really happened many times. In my own hole I would rub out one after another into my hand, the cum getting lost in all the sweat and occasional blood, which I liked because it was good, for days and weeks after such encounters, which blossomed into high romances in my heart. These were the pinnacle, the closest to my ideal, and when I discov-ered that it was really possible to advance on such peo-ple and actually know them, touch them, I felt a deeply humble sense of privilege, awed gratitude and happiness that was unquestionably the emotional zenith of my life and was very obviously only possible in some degree or state of ignorance, and therefore confined forever to the past.

As I learned the slum tongue I told a hundred benign lies which I could never keep track of. I learned the sim-ple narratives that oiled the grooves we moved along, I learned what was expected or assumed and had been codified about men and women and the men of my race in particular. I want to describe my affair with Aunty

Ot. (It isn't fuck trophies, adventure stories, pervert qualifications. I do have to constantly check myself. I thought about Ot continuously throughout our affair as a woman and a person, as member of a family, as having been born before me, and as someone who stepped outside reductive categories quite easily.) Ot is important to me. I want to make her breathe into this so she can breathe forever in acknowledgement of her beauty and her kindness, and her race, skin tone, obesity and social class, which were all and are still sexual organs.

Ot is the fattest woman I've ever touched, truly obese, but smooth-skinned, clean and impossibly well formed – a fat person whose physique appears as though it were intentionally designed in line with a deliberate code of beauty. This aesthetic obesity, oiled, cultivated and maintained, might be comparable to U Po Kyin in *Burmese Days*. Ot lived in a hovel near mine with a number of younger relatives that ran over and around her like puppies, and she would sit like an engorged and smiling fay in the entrance of the hovel, sometimes partially veiled by a diaphanous curtain of frayed, sun-bleached vinyl. Her sensual thick-lipped smile was flanked by deep-hanging powdery jowls that were each seasoned by small clusters of dimples. The sun would sparkle on her long black hair, which fell down her body like a waterfall of crude oil. Her form and its dimensions were simply beyond breasts. Her bust is nameless in the manner that God cannot be represented with visual fidelity. I spilled such quantities of sperm in states of solitary ecstasy to the memory of her clothed body alone, as I am describing it now, before I ever touched or saw her bare nipples, to which at that time I attributed a fatal quality, fearing even to imagine them, that I might burst into flame if the mystery were ever revealed, which was my only defence against the almost unbearable desire I felt to disassemble myself into every corner of her and then be extinct into sexual oblivion. The skin that flowed like cream behind her deftly fastened sarongs and belts of silk would ripple like honey-milk in a bag of tanned hide as she laughed over the drone of her miniature television set.

The novelty of my presence there amongst the corrugated iron and tarpaulin had worn away by the time I let go my physical body into Ot. I moved in a manner that deliberately expressed the illusion I wrapped myself in. I dusted my body in turmeric and waxed my moustache. I huffed petrol and vomited in full view of others, smoked my tobaccos in foreign and ostentatious ways. Ot laughingly rejected me the first few times I suggested we have sex, in a perfectly expressed rolling train of gestures that conveyed all of her idle pleasure and surprise in my interest, her agreement to have an affair, and her profound equanimity in regard to its meaning. It was perfect.

I flailed and dribbled little tributes on her sixty-year-old genius like a baby seal. I had no boring porno agenda, I was in a total state of nature. Her areola was as large as my hand, her nipple filled my suckling mouth, impervious to my assertions. I loosed myself on her skin. An arm was another breast with no nipple. A breast like a sand dune. My limbs spontaneously detached and washed away. I gave my gnarled and rigid penis to be clamped in her plump claw. She pulled quilts of skin under my crotch in an overture to my tight, sensitive nuts, but to submerge in the depths of another silken limb. The waters of our bodies wobble and parts hopelessly overlap. No separate lines, bones joined where they collided in violence, calcified and sunk deep. Here a warm fold, a fragrant crevice, the taut skin of a huge drum, shallow ranges of distance and deserts of milk. Suddenly aware of something in my mouth. I just squirmed on her. To locate myself. Which I couldn't reach. Wriggled and bucked and lapped with total abandon (I have since lost the courage to unfold myself like this). Cram my tongue deep into a nostril and go limp as my chin and neck are sprayed hard with moist, perfumed breath. In a dank windowless concrete box that smelled of musty blankets and her children's urine.

Don't think I ever actually was aware of her vagina, and probably never entered it. Most times we wriggled and rubbed ourselves lost together and I released sperm in some soft fold or elsewhere that didn't matter and she would giggle and rumble softly, immersing and sealing us over into hours of indolent paralysis. In the mornings, when I could feel myself in my own separate body again, she would roll on top of me like a great sea lion or a tent of warm jelly and slip my penis into her mouth like a lozenge. Her lips puckered and enveloped, her tongue stroked and with a smooth and natural rhythm contained in a rapid and barely perceptible outward movement, she worked my length for long tolerant minutes until I shot off deep into nowhere and everything. I could feel myself disintegrate. I loved her furiously in those minutes, and I cherish her memory forever in the highest baroque corridors of the pantheon.

Nuances of value rise to the surface of my memory as I write this down. I had to do the hard work first, something I never gave myself much credit for. What I'm sure is important in terms of where I started from though, is that at the time it wasn't work. It was wanking. But it isn't so simple as to say that writing *per se* has become performative, or that experience has become the object of writing assignments. The detail in piles of reeking slum waste was an innocuous element that formed a base, or self-generating scenery, within which to locate the greater figurative works of slum architecture and molten celestials like Ot. I was convinced that Oriental female obesity was the highest virtue, the most valuable, the greatest pleasure I could expect, and the most secret, and that Ot was *the only* fat Oriental woman in the respect that she eclipsed and replaced all others. I look now at the decaying matter of leaves and dead wood that lie around me here, which has such an apparently different value, and I wonder what the difference is and where precisely it's located; how important it is, and why it's capable of generating the same sexual essence as a gutted and rotting mattress crawling with tiny brown flies. A hundred eruptions of smashed tiles and cement chunks that have seeped up and out of the churning ground like lava and frozen into expressions of chaos and discomfort. A load of old luggage and handbags and pastel-coloured upholstered jewellery boxes scattered like confetti. A hillock of neatly tied plastic bags full of rotten fish, swarming with huge clumsy flies the colour of onyx and serpentine. A sodden cardboard folder of documents and photocopied pictures of cars. Some rolls of negative film and three deformed photographs of ladyboys in a bar. Smashed flowerpots. Old spirit-houses leaned against the trunks of sugar palms, brightly coloured gauze and other ravaged pieces of material. Toothbrushes. Juice cartons. A piece of collapsed MDF furniture with smashed shards of mirror. Blister packs of medicine, full and empty, their decomposed cardboard packaging. Circuit boards. Big fresh dollops of cow shit. Explosions of filthy sponge from upholstering, food and rice sacks, a rotting dog's corpse full of maggots. And everything fixed and tied exactly where it is by fresh growths of wild herbs and grasses, and nauseatingly animated by large dragonflies and colourful butterflies that fill the baking air like shoals of fish over a coral reef.

The mountain is mine, it is made in my image, and I deserve it. Siamese cosmology identifies the centre of everything, the place of all origins, as a great axial strut, a pillar, crowned by the red sun and with a subterranean egg at its base. It is the pivot around and through which all cycles occur, a mountain corpus, a vast serpent, an absolute organ of reproduction and the purest concentration of power. It is a hydraulic post, whose arteries channel solar breath and water through the head, lungs and heart of the macrocosm. Its structure is replicated in all organisation, and especially in the human body and all architectural forms. An architectonic language describes the facilities of the body, and the sexual politics of the body are inherent in all buildings. When they erect even the lowliest structure, the first or primary post is ritually installed as a microcosmic reproduction of the absolute centre. Chips taken from this post in ceremonies are carried as amulets.

A community of gypsies used to camp in the woods behind my house in Scotland when I was a child. A great, steep embankment rose up beyond our fenced garden with its rhododendron bushes and dry stone walls. It formed one side of the valley around our housing scheme and was accessible to vehicles via a wide gateway in the old Abbey wall whose wooden door hung open and rotten. I was forbidden to go into that part of the woods on their account, but often we went to make contact with them in groups led by elder boys. The adults were always drunk inside the caravans, and we would scatter if one appeared. The teenagers were friendly enough though, despite their incomprehensibility. We took their cigarettes and pornography, but wouldn't touch their proffered bottles with our lips. Whenever the police cleared them out again we would spend days combing the derelict camp, collecting anything smokable and burning their old clothes and other rubbish in their readymade campfires. Sometimes they left really good stuff – petrol, tools, cash-and-carry packs of matches and so forth.

I still have a fragment of porn that came from them pritt-sticked into a scrapbook. It shows a woman with her breasts poking out of special holes in an armless leather garment, sucking on a dildo. All the gypsy porn was like this – from sex magazines rather than page three or other softcore. At the time there seemed to be a trend for tearing up and tossing pornography randomly around lesser visited public space – the woods, dumps, tunnels, old buildings, industrial estates and so on. We would make daring pilgrimages to these places and collect, transport and reinstall the relics we found there.

Around my village are several corrugated-iron slums and settlements that house Burmese and Shan refugees and hill people. I like to spy on them, and though I'm delighted when I happen upon their colourful rituals, I just like to see them, to *be near* them, smell them, their chickens and the smoke from their fires.

Finally, yesterday morning, stood on a footboard over a shallow stream of sewage, I was introduced to a plump tattooed Burmese called Sen who was to introduce me to a witch I was hoping to interview in an ethnographic capacity. Prompted to explain myself, I told

Sen that I wanted help with a bothersome legal issue. Sen prepared to make a telephone call from his mobile phone, explaining that he would call the witch's servant and request a visit. I asked about the servant and Sen told me he was a fourteen-year-old boy from the mountains who lived with the witch as its assistant, and dealt with its telephone requests, which had to be made prior to a visit. I asked him to tell me more about the witch itself and what to expect. He answered casually that he didn't really know very much about it and he had never been up into the witch's house. He only ever spoke to the boy-servant, passing on the details of a request, and then delivered the favour-seeker to the house, which I was very surprised to learn was not so far away off a trail I knew very well from my wandering. I knew the specific house and had looked up at it many times: it was a relatively old, dark wooden house with a jutting arched roof and a wide veranda built on tall stilts, right on the swell of the mountain, into whose heavy coat of leaves it extended. I'd always assumed the house was lying vacant. He made the call in a language I wasn't familiar with, and after pausing for many tension-building minutes in the middle, finally confirmed to me that we could approach the house five hours later, at noon. He then asked for a hundred baht tip for himself.

Noon arrived, and Sen parked some fifty yards or so from the wooden house, which was taller and more gaunt, darker, and more strikingly esoteric in design than it had been before. Sen alighted from his vulgar truck and beckoned me to stand with him in front of it, in silent suspense. Some time passed in which I studied the unusual shapes formed by the wooden slats of the structure's frontage, and its frightening, black jut of a roof, which suggested to me a rearing, eyeless shark.

Then a crisp, shrill tone emitted from a reed instrument of some kind and the entrance to the house that led onto the broad teak balcony slid open, revealing a wooden darkness, as dry as my mouth. Two figures emerged out into the light. The house, the silence, the note from the reed instrument and the appearance were quite beautiful and faultlessly choreographed, and from this opening I knew with great investment and certainty that whatever followed would be a work of applied genius. The distance we stood at and the height of the balcony made the figures only just visible. The boy wore a red sarong and his head was wrapped in a red cloth.

The vision of the witch itself was more impressive than I'd expected. Its nude body was a milky greenish white, and I realised it was an albino. It was without a single hair anywhere. It was totally androgynous; I could detect neither breasts, nipples nor any sign of genitalia. Its hands were indiscernible behind wiry tangles of overgrown brown and yellow fingernails. It was blind; its large almond eyes were clouded over with the same shade of milk as its body. It had no nose protrusion, only two tiny nostril curls, like flourishes on a sculpture. Its mouth was lipless, a shut slit.

As I walked forward in unison with Sen, our pace slowing with every step, the witch seemed to glisten horribly in the sunlight, giving it a commanding and ghostly clarity. I saw that this effect was produced by what first seemed like scales on its body, but then conceded to be pieces of gauze wrapped tight round its trunk. As Sen stopped so did I, jumping slightly as the witch began to sway rhythmically from side to side like a snake. The movement was inhuman. Very suddenly its jaw clicked and its mouth gaped horribly open, ejecting a great mouthful of fire into the air like a flamethrower. The streak of fire separated like liquid as it fell onto the dust in front of us, burning away until only a dense clump of small flames endured, which then began to move haltingly, inch by inch toward us as if drawn by a jerky magnet. As the flames died away completely they revealed a singed, black scorpion, still struggling forward and belching oily smoke. It not give, said Sen, gently guiding me backwards. Oh yes it give, I thought, yes it fucking well give.

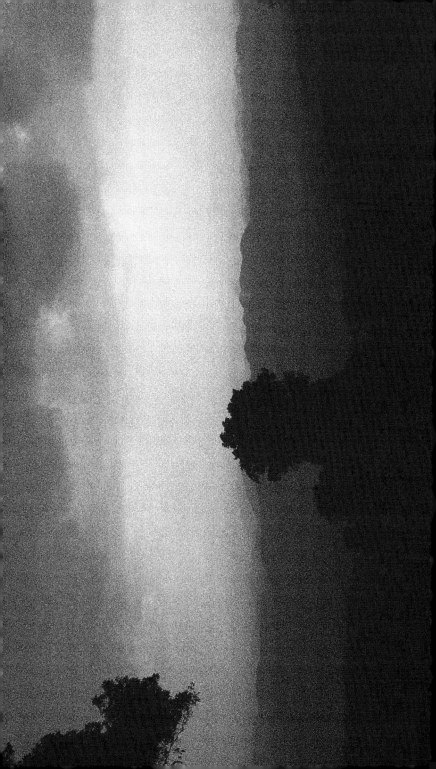

I try to build an image of a man and a woman that su-
perimposes itself over a perfect grid of bunded paddies,
a grid so precise that the blocks of colour and light in
their perfection burn through the image. I'm looking
at the squares of water from beside and among them
(this is a place that I pass most days), I can see the luminous green and purple fronds that pepper some of them
(for the grid is now lying fallow or abandoned, and the
fronds are the beginning of a natural reclamation), and
I can see the Vast Southern Aspect of the mountain reflected there in these liquid squares. I better appreciate
the kinetic evil contained in the dark green velvet of
the mountain's coat when I examine it reflected in this
clear, agricultural grid. Divided into squared sections
which are never complete, I find it easier to distinguish
its meanings and confront them systematically, one at a
time, responsibly. Washes of light and water, no matter
how dramatic and picturesque, no matter how intox-
icating, can never threaten the integrity of the scenes
and images that I see there. And slowly turning my face,
there it actually is in the sky behind me *right now*, the
mountain, shimmering through the hot blue in all of its
secretive menace.

At dusk, as I swept my veranda free of lizard shit and
leaves, a large black scorpion scuttled out from a corner.

I had never seen one so large before, black as tar, a tank of an arachnid, every portion of its body plated with armour or ending in a weapon. I cannot think of a more elegantly martial-looking species, in spite of the slow, clunky register in which they move – the price of such equipment. I sidestepped the scorpion as it recoiled slightly, and walked around to the kitchen. I picked up the domed glass lid of my electric cooking pot from the sink rack and came back at the scorpion from behind. I placed the lid over the animal and weighted it to the ground with a rock, examined it further for a minute or two and then retired for the evening.

The following morning I smoked heavily in bed after huffing some petrol and eating a sour mango. Emerging from the veils of my insect netting like a tobacco princess heavy with urine, I saw three more scorpions on the floor, what the fuck. Shocked, I took an umbrella and bashed them to death one by one, spiking the last one with the tip as it tried to un-mangle itself like an obscene mechanical toy in the centre of its execution-tile. I gathered up the corpses in their slimy armour and put them in a piece of folded paper. Opening the door to eject them out onto the maw of the forest floor, I was struck to see biblical rivers of scorpions, each one squat, determined and stupid, making the earth move with nausea as they advanced with grinding effort in all directions. I picked up my shoes and stamped on each toe to make sure it was empty. I turned on the hose at the front of the veranda and blasted the animals away in waves, drenching the veranda and the kitchen. I sprayed my motorcycle clean for good measure, started it up and rolled out of the orchard crunching claws and armour under my tyres as I went in a state of wondrous disgust.

Every trail through the village was encrusted with flattened and dying scorpions. As I passed villagers on bikes and in side-cars they pointed to the road grinning as though I might not have noticed what was occurring. Small fires burnt along the road and in yards and gardens to repel the creatures. I pulled around to join the inter-village road, heading toward the Shan settlement. Slowing down to light a cigarette I passed a forestry official conscientiously sweeping scorpions alive and dead out of his booth and its surrounds. I imagined collecting all the dead and dying scorpions on barrows, shovelling them up into packages and dragging them to the bare strip of wasteland behind the charnel ground. I would build the scorpions into a giant stupa, a black tower of claws and stingers, plate armour and oozing flesh, with a great domed base and a sharp crown. Over the first twenty-four hours some of the legs and stingers would still be twitching, and the oily fluids and armour would glint in the sunlight.

When I arrived back at the lodge, I was received by the scorpion in its glass dome. I swept inside the bedroom for arachnids and lit a long cheroot on the veranda. I tormented the scorpion by pushing it one way and another by moving the glass lid, and freeing it for a few seconds at a time, dropping the lid again when it began to move. It was the first scorpion, and consequently it appeared bigger and more completely formed than the hundreds of others that had followed it. I picked up the domed lid again and used it to guide the animal into a plastic bowl, which I carried over to the shallow ravine that demarcates the west side of the orchard. I flipped it up, out, into the air and it sailed down gracefully between two trees into the tall wild grasses.

The lodge is situated with its back to the mountain. Its cement base is set into the gentle gradient of the mountain's skirt, the visual sense of which is choked by trees and ivy-carpeted ravines and ditches. One must know the topography well in order to feel the mountain, to have a sense of its proximity, its immensity, and therefore to partake of the anxiety I feel in my awareness of its vast expanse and height from within the lodge.

The orchard is bordered from the mountain proper by an old fence of bamboo and rusted barbed wire. There is a hole halfway along the fence: my ceremonial gate between garden and forest. The outer shell of a policeman's helmet has been impaled on the bamboo pole closest to the gate, a marker, of which I feel an odd sense of possessive ownership (I often think to myself as I pass the helmet, I am within my rights to remove that, and employ it to my own ends). I crawled through the gate into the mountain, with rice and tobacco in my bag. I have still not purged myself of Cambodia.

I could have entered the forest from between the brick factory and the reservoir, climbing up a green embankment from the mud path that runs around the water, and navigate a u-shaped route that takes me to the barbed-wire gate from the other side. I sometimes take this route for the sake of variety and exercise if walking back home from the village. There is a steep section of hill, mostly ashen and bare from fires at this time of year, that is capped by a slim plateau about six metres wide, which then rises again behind a convenient wall of well-spaced, young Acacia trees.

I sit and imagine a huge statue of Pod. It would be forty feet tall and of course be made from concrete. It would be unpainted but smooth, with rashes of lichen and moisture damage. Pod would be depicted in a neutral attitude, standing straight with his arms at his sides, fingers together. The body would be very slightly elongated, lending it a folkish quality and ironing out some of the bulk from the upper-body musculature.

Four thick upright poles would form a framework around the statue, with the dimensions of a perfectly oblong coffin or a sentry box, connected by a series of thick, diagonally welded horizontal bars that cross each other, impaling and holding the statue through seven points up and down the central axis of the body, the lowest protruding from the shins and the highest from the cheeks. Back down by the reservoir, on the dirt track that skirts the water, I imagine a painted plastic sign nailed to a tree that would say *Poderic De Newbury*, with an arrow underneath pointing the way.

Pod found Baphomet's scarred, lusty, bruised body, the crude, affected gestures of femininity, the callous wit, the stench of hyena piss, alcohol psychosis, violence, the screaming fits that caused urine to weep from her bulbous vulva, staining her market-knickers, her bullet nipples lolling like pegs on a line from her bony rib-cage, and her stretch-marked, ruined, rice-soup navel, in Cambodia.

We visited her family in their slum: her silent, skeletal father, her fat, turbaned mother's piles for which we handed over clinic and witch-doctor fees, her healthy, solid brother Atoon with his long fingernails and his slim wife, who asked me if white women bled once a month like Khmer women did.

Pod watched, taciturn like the others and I, as Baphomet slapped the face of her niece, making the child scream and cry (it reminded me of a bus journey between Phnom Penh and Battambang. A Khmer mother began hitting her crying baby, making it cry louder and more desperately, to which the mother responded with harder and more desperate blows. Unable to take the debauched spectacle, a French tourist got up from her seat at the back and gingerly approached the woman, uselessly reasoning in French. I sank deeper into my seat with fatigue as the baby's grandmother pulled it from the grip of her daughter in embarrassment).

That night on the dusty road, a group of child prostitutes emerged from an alleyway making sucking gestures, whispering low prices in American dollars. I can't believe how tiny they are, how good their English is, how charmed and frightened I am by them (there is no justification for alarm – nobody cares except the handful of old women NGOs drinking their gin at the Foreign Correspondent's Club – child porn can be purchased openly at roadside stalls in the centre of town). I cover my crotch from their groping in embarrassment, as my mind struggles to formulate a more assertive and appropriate response.

Then Baphomet struck the faces of these blowjob children, making them cry, and then in what I think was some appalling sublimation she began to weep and strike Pod in her rage and embarrassment. Pod had moved reflexively to give some money to two of the lingering cocksuckers. I was wary of hidden eyes and the treachery of even the stones and rubbish in the street.

A tuk-tuk appeared and we climbed in, back to the safety of the lake. The driver was drunk, sliding over the road in arrogant, sweeping curves, horn wailing like a tortured cat, and a new fear was born straight out of the other with equally intense and distressing noise. Soon enough, the driver pulled us out into oncoming traffic on Norodom Boulevard and a speeding motorbike thunked into us broadside. Our carriage rolled, torn asunder, and I felt my body pulled and pushed and thrown inside the tight space as we hurtled round and around.

Pod emerged first, put Baphomet gently down on the ground and examined her bleeding leg. Then I climbed out, my limbs shaking, rearranging my bag absurdly over my shoulder. Twenty feet away the driver was screaming about his cut legs, which were stuck in the severed thorax of the tuk-tuk, fuel spilling out dangerously from between them. I looked at the two helmeted bodies from the motorbike, which had itself disappeared somewhere. They were metres apart from each other on the road, twisted and dead.

Pod was unhurt. Baphomet was sitting on the curb and I was stunned. A ring of onlookers – a crowd – had collected. I paced slowly, testing my body with the movements, as Pod tended to Baphomet and the crowd grew larger and larger. There was a numb tension in the air as we and the crowd waited for what would happen next.

Baphomet stood up as six helmeted policemen pulled up on motorbikes: six thin-armed teenagers in ill-fitting khaki, rubber sandals and weathered AK-47s strapped tightly over their shoulders. For a second I wanted to stay with the policemen, I wanted to bask in the danger of their attention, to be associated with them, to hold my own in the water with them, and make them benignly interested in me with some virtuoso display of my involvement. I wanted to help them, to be extended privileges by them, to be known as a friend of the *Cambodian National Police.*

I caught Pod's gaze and these notions disappeared. We quietly, carefully moved together, holding each other's hands, into the crowd, completely ignored by the policemen. Further down the wide boulevard, Baphomet hailed two motos. I sat on mine with a feeling of intense relief, smelling the driver's unwashed hair and letting the wind dry my sweat, and we alighted at the hole in the wall by the mosque with its baying sheep, and walked the rest of the way smoking.

On the jetty, we lit cigarettes at our table and waited for the beers we had ordered. The staff bandaged Baphomet's leg as she rattled off the story, and then went to play pool on her favourite table. I got up to take a tired long-held piss and splash water on my face.

As I was returning a shriek rang out across the jetty followed by urgent Khmer shouting. Pod was over the pool table, plucking Baphomet's wrists from the air, causing her to drop the glass, which smashed apart on the planks below. Standing up, my heart sank as I saw the girl that Baphomet had cut bent over the table and clutching her face, which was bleeding onto the green felt. As I pushed my way through to the table, friends of the cut prostitute attacked Pod and Baphomet with glasses and pool cues in unison. The way they sprung into motion made me think of a coin-operated, moving diorama in a children's theme restaurant. Their blows grazed off Pod as he restrained the wriggling and furious Baphomet and made sober placations on her behalf.

I didn't feel very much at the beginning of the brawl other than irritation at Baphomet. I was drunk and tired and it was all too silly, as horrible violence can often seem at first. Some tourists fled, but many remained and joined in the senseless loss of restraint and malevolent lunacy that brawls typically give rise to. A Swedish maniac and some fat American expatriate used the occasion to beat one of the less popular waiters with pool cues and palm fronds and throw him in the lake. The Khmer youths and tuk-tuk drivers who had come in from outside were in a frenzy of assault, hitting anyone and everyone within reach, with anything that came to hand. A lanky European woman was screaming and holding her face. I saw Map, our friendly barman standing in his usual place at the bar with his arms folded in weary disapproval. His stillness became a dramatic foreshadowing of Pod's, which was right then born in a maculate bronze aspect over the table; he was twice his size, the hammer-work of his arms, buttocks and thighs, the escutcheon of *moral violence* contained in muscular discipline.

But as every fibre of Baphomet rebelled against the categorical restraint of Pod's embrace, so the clench of his body became an emblem of regret, of naïveté, of great sadness under the wrath of Cambodia, which is like a mad and starved dog that can only be abandoned.

I was captured there too. I saw I would have to follow Pod's embrace of Baphomet. She'd obviously been right to cut the girl.

A Norwegian man sought to intercede on Baphomet's behalf. He wouldn't listen to my explanation of Pod's sensitive heraldry or Cambodia's wild melancholy as *woman*, and so as I stepped from his path, I spiked him hard in the neck with my elbow. Feet stamped, fists clenched and stabbed, eyes rolled, the jetty was beginning to disassemble under our movement. The black water of the lake churned underneath us.

Then a girl I'd vaguely admired around the place spoke my name. She'd been hit in the stomach, and suggested we hide in my room. Her fragility seemed so authentic and tender. I chaperoned her off the jetty, into the corridor that led to my room. Her hand in mine, in this low passage with its smell of dank concrete, neutralised the petty concerns of the brawl and humbled me again into the uncertainty and wonder of youth. I'd been charged with the protection of a comely angel. Inside my cell there was little in the way of props to assist my chivalry. I cleaned her face and arms with a moistened towel and lay her out on the bed, which I covered with a blanket before climbing inside myself. We lay there in silence, unable to speak to each other. The brawl melted away completely under the whirring electrical drones of the room, which was windowless and lit with a single, weak lightbulb attached to the wall over the bed. These things had a sedative effect on me, and my mind began slowly to revolve without conscious participation. Rows and rows of photographed children's faces. Twisted death on Norodom Boulevard.

So it was, that I was surprised when her hand began to stroke my thigh, this wounded baby with dead parents, this antidote to Baphomet's wild, angry, ignorant power. Her head turned to face mine, her black eyes widely spaced like a rabbit's, and she smiled at me. It wasn't a lascivious gesture, it was full and intimate, expectant and sincere. She made some subtle movements with her body, flexes, exhalations, that drew attention to the extent of her physicality lying there beside me, untouched and alive. I put my hand gently on her stomach and she smiled again. Our clothing fell away. I was hard and flaky as painted iron, and she was dark brown and dusty. Her skin smelt of un-perfumed earth, her breasts were healthy and full, filling and responding to my hands as she climbed on top of me, hugging my ribcage with her thighs. I looked at her cunt in front of my face. The hairs were thick and sparse, the lips almost black, with a birthmark on the crease of her inner thigh. I touched the lips gently, and slipped a finger inside. I pushed three fingers together against the pubic pad, feeling her clit and making her breathe sharply.

Before I came inside her I tried to focus solely on what her vaginal walls felt like on my shaft and helmet. Every ridge and mottled lump, every glandular concentration, every string of bubbly mucous. I found her stomach, back, thighs, neck and arms quite as lush as her breasts as I drank her flesh with my hands. And her mouth. Her eyes never left mine; I was not permitted to fall into the usual spaces to arm myself alone, to sift fussily through images. There was still some blood on her hand. I didn't mind, but it made me think of the two people whose deaths we'd played a role in that evening. What was the condition of their blood now? Was it cooling inside the fridge of the city's only hospital, or slowly coagulating at the side of the road in the heat? Collecting gradually into networks of stringy, lumpy matter, and then quantities of dry, degraded protein paste? This paste in my mind, and the uneven topography of her vagina, were together in a relationship that my reverberating cock caught and whipped into its rhythm.

How old did I think the children were? I thought the eldest was maybe ten. How many were there? I thought five or six, but I wasn't sure. They were small and thin, dark, and dirty. They could speak English well, and they knew how to give a blowjob. This matters to me. One of the children was performing this gesture of wanking or rubbing the shaft of a cock into his open, empty, dry little mouth, and the register of movement, the physical gesture, looked so natural and free of style. No lust or performance. The only meaning contained in the movement itself was responsive and economic.

The children were prostitutes. They were a gang of trained mouth-whores, who scuttled out from a dark passageway in which their Fagan probably lurked, rubbing her Chinese gun with a rag. How long does it take to train a child to give an adult a blowjob? How long does it take to teach an adult to train a child to give an adult a blowjob? What are the ruses and horrible tricks of it? Is it less hideous than we think, in reality? Ghastly, but in the end just flesh against flesh, organic algebra deep out of sight in the food-chain, flowers opening and closing, before drooping and drying out. Do they feel what we read as *trauma*, as the years pile up, or is it accommodated with ease, quite preferable to hunger and thirst and being hit? Such knowledge exists in the world, these people and things are real, and whether they matter or not, they have intruded inside my real life and my sexuality.

Baphomet was born to be a hooker, her degenerate, animal violence was matched by her articulate charisma, and was adapted to absorb and process damage into something edible. Three months after she miscarried Pod's child in another motor accident, she used the rest of the money he'd given her to move her extended family of some twenty people into an unfinished concrete row of rooms on some farmland in Sihanoukville.

The day before we left Phnom Penh to move there permanently, Baphomet climbed the six floors to my room with some cursed gifts. The first was a bowl of noodles and banana flowers which gave me mild food-poisoning. The second was a scorpion inside a closed lotus bud. Here's your new wife if you want, said Baphomet. Take her or leave her. She's coming with us anyway, to Sihanoukville, where she has a bar. Her name is Gon.

The structure was a mere outer shell, but it had an intermittent supply of electricity and running water. The bunded paddies surrounding the site were picturesque in their green luminosity and red earth. Baphomet had arranged for me to rent the room next to Pod's bridal suite for fifty US dollars a month. I also rented a motorbike and went into town to visit Gon and buy some ice on that first afternoon. We might live here happily after all, I thought. Parking at the market, I realised that the key had slid out and was lost. A one-armed security guard pointed to a stall across the street that could make a new one for a dollar. In the market, the only ice I could find was sold in fat, dripping paving slabs, so I bought one wrapped in cloth and held it between my legs as I rode home, where Pod and I smashed it up with an axe. In the evening, drinking around a fire, Baphomet laid down another routine of health issues and well-mannered extortion, which I allowed even my distinguished self to be caught inside.

Only a day later, Pod decided he was going to leave Baphomet. He offered me the money I'd be losing on the rent. Due to Baphomet's psychotic nature, the best option before going back to Phnom Penh appeared to be going to Gon's bar and staying with her, although I had misgivings about this because it would lead to my becoming definitively encumbered with her at least while I was here. Pod locked his pack and gear in my room along with what I couldn't carry and we walked the length of the building to my bike, seeing Atoon and the others listening in silent neutrality to Baphomet's destruction of Pod's former bridal suite. This savage, unsophisticated violence cast a shadow of ghastly menace across my mind. It made Gon's star glow warmly, charting out the way through the cracked laterite and rice fields to the bar district.

On a ghostly stretch of road we were pulled over by two policemen who took a four dollar bite out of me for not wearing a helmet or having a license. A third cop sat in the upper branches of a tree smoking, his gaze trained on the snaking highway for more foreign prey. The bony earth of the Cambodian landscape was constantly being defiled and re-defiled I thought, and I knew that the police treasured terror as their institutional heritage, and my mind wandered around sketches of their childhoods and dead parents. I felt their grip on the land in my heart with admiration.

Gon sat at the centre of her small fiefdom like a haughty princess, her comely mother nursing Gon's infant child: the bastard heir to her throne drawn from the sack of a withered Englishman milked to a husk and tossed to another young mamasan under-queen in a neighbouring bar. I marvelled again at the genius of a smiling teenage cop who interrupted our audience to collect his protection fee. Gon sent two of her girls to arrange another shell of a room for Pod, and another two girls to the market with a handful of my money to buy the ingredients for a banquet of fried meat. And it was done, I'd sold myself to a whore, a savage every bit as ugly inside as Baphomet, whose mango-breasts in their jiggling stupidity were to be the only counterweight to my hatred of her. Pod and I chain-smoked and drank French wine as a lesbian hairdresser in Gon's court painted strategically dramatic images of Baphomet's motivation and capability for revenge.

The items locked in my room back at Baphomet's row were as follow: one red tin of wax, a knockoff photocopy of *Cambodia's Bad Frenchmen*, an axe and a plastic bag of dirty vests. Also Pod's full pack, and a heavy, black metal chin-up bar designed to be slotted over the top of a door. Pod and I set off after dark on my bike to retrieve these items with two of Gon's minions in tow on another bike. We were wine-drunk, anxious and tired.

I turned off the engine and let the bike roll down the mud trail in neutral. There was some light from a fire outside the row, apart from which the darkness of the fields was complete. Gaggles of family were sitting in small groups. There was a monotonous drone of frogs and cicadas. I ignored the peasants, unlocked the door alertly and we collected the items and divided them between Pod and Gon's servants. He hauled the pack with the chin-up bar hooked into a strap on the back. The girls started their machine and began up the trail and I began to feel the giddiness of success. I let go the room's padlock key arrogantly into the mud and started the bike. Pod climbed on behind.

I felt the bike jump forward as Baphomet pulled Pod from the back, effortlessly using the weight of the pack, and as I turned in panic the bike fell on its side and the new key again slipped from the ignition. I could see Baphomet beating Pod viciously with the chin-up bar, and his embarrassing screams of outraged distress. My heart clenched tight with panic.

The mute smears of family began to move in. Atoon's silhouette loomed uncertainly behind his wife's. Baphomet turned and swung the bar at me but hit the bike, smashing out the light, and decided to try to take out the vehicle completely. Using the fraction of time it took for her to reconfigure her swing, I punched her titless chest sharply, knocking the wind out of her. I got ready for Atoon, but he didn't come. I pulled Pod up, and his whole face was crimson with blood. I found the key and started the bike. Pod climbed on bleeding, and Baphomet rose again screaming from the mud, to pull us down a second time. Furious, I punched her in the face this time and Pod held her down in the dirt as I pulled the bike up again, kick-started the engine and juggered in first gear toward the shut curtain of Baphomet's family, who parted slowly to let me pass and did not close themselves again. Pod got on the bike as Baphomet again stood up, but we had secured the short measure of distance we needed and I willed the worn-out tyres of my battered machine to shoot flecks of gravel back down the trail into Baphomet's eyes.

After gunning the bike full throttle over several junctions I pulled in to a petrol station to wash and bandage Pod's face, which I cradled with the jagged sentiment of drunken shock. One of several American voices behind us exclaimed, and I gave a rude warning in overcompensation. The voice responded with further insensitivity and intrusive volume, and I marvelled at my own thuggishness as I turned and punched it wildly in the face. The pain in my knuckles and my sudden fear of a new confrontation exploded into an inwardly jeering triumph as I saw the feeble Americans cower in the panic of my assault. The surge flipped just as quickly into shame and self-disgust when I saw the weary disapproval in Pod's eyes behind the bloody snot and bubbles. I helped him back on the bike, and silence set in as we cruised the last miles back to safety. In those moments as they passed, and in the long nights that followed, I rubbed myself all over this act and recoiled again and again as it distorted and grew out into and around the themes of the memories and the choices we'd made, and hardened into a gummy pellet that was lost in my body, that I could never pass, that I forgot and remembered again in every minute that ticked off, that made my mind a captive inside the beast of myself. I disgusted myself so thoroughly. I was never so self-aware as Pod's gaze made me, and at this moment now, in my retreat, I find that he has supernaturally assumed partial ownership of this act. Are these the routines of a ubiquitous, common or garden bore who trades low-grade charisma, old-hand experience and daytime-television mythology for drinks in the first-stop tourist bars of these Asian cities? I promise I am really trying very hard here to develop a body of text possessed of more than one dimension.

In my room I felt like the adolescent Paris fleeing Sparta: wanted, doomed, inside a short, tight breathing space before a barbaric and justified public execution; I felt the reality of our violence, and the violence visited on us, done, undertaken, rippling out in imbricated mandalas of consequence as we breathed right there in those moments, hopelessly whittling down the future into only the most drastic and desperate of choices, again. And then Pod was largely wordless and immovable, I found that he was not present, as he stoically considered his new living arrangements and career options. Was he internally censuring me? Or had my redemption begun even then? (In the corridor that led to the toilet and living quarters behind Gon's bar, I was paralysed by the sight of a giant spider on the wall. Its long, cantilevered legs spread out from a breast-plated thorax, from which its pert lower body sprouted like a hideous grape. Its poise, the obscene composition of its legs and body against the wall, was the very emblem of pollution. I was truly helpless, a wretch. Pod destroyed the animal for me, and my gratitude to him for this will be eternal.)

Gon's court closed its thorny limbs around us. It was her town and her friends were everywhere, studded through the Institution's grapevine, all the way to Baphomet. Spies and masked actors came to deliver their reports, the former whispering in Gon's ear, the latter performing ritual theatre so as to make the party line very clear and unquestionable – Baphomet was consumed with the desire for revenge and intended to use the remaining money Pod had given her to hire two cheap assassins in the form of moto drivers. Gon advised that we go to ground under her care, and not leave the bar at night. Every Khmer man on a motorbike was suspect, thus the bus station would be suicide. Baphomet would give up in time, accept the deadlock that Gon's protection represented, and go back to Phnom Penh.

My contempt for Gon's predatory efficiency, peasant ignorance and needy vagina would greatly increase after our dependence on her was sealed by a horrific incident. One morning, I left the bar to buy a cup of fresh coffee in a restaurant down the way. I noticed a Khmer man in a flak jacket follow me on his motorbike, though I was at first unconcerned as not only was this behaviour consistent with that of any moto driver outside a bar for foreigners, but I still held that the threat described to us was primarily designed as an extractive tool. Drinking my coffee I watched him adjust his belt under the jacket as he fidgeted outside, revealing a glimpse of a shitty little Chinese pistol of the make that all Khmer criminals seem to favour. Adrenal fear flushed through me like a huff of petrol. I latched onto a group of men leaving, and returned to the bar.

The hours of days and nights became inseparable and endless burning cigarettes, cups of red wine and plates of fried red meat. As Pod left through the priest hole after each tired session, Gon would come into my room like a man in the night.

And I do recognise that Gon elucidates *my* failure during the Cambodian era to find something better and new in and of my self-celebrated access. Whores were apparently for me just as they were for the despicable others: *Justines* – pure victims whose flaws and faults, if any were visible, were due to specifically circumstantial abuse and damage, whose sufferings processed their femininity into something dependently stupid, weak and attractive. Or hustlers. Vicious animals – sharks and hyenas unresponsive to reason, sly, rapid, fundamentally criminal and parasitic, baser, so much more deeply below and beyond my silly aesthetic hierarchies. You and your rape stories and your dead sisters and Pol Pot were all just my own private art gallery, until this motivated killer with a gun. With each mouthful of wine the algebra of whores and johns and Asia inverts again, with each new cunt or anus ploughed and tit bitten, banknote exchanged, the dyadic relationship between whores and johns breaks down, blurs, intersects, flips from one to the other's benefit, agency, victimhood, choice, fault, nature.

I don't know how I was capable of getting hard for Gon, or why our sex was so frequent and protracted. She continually berated me and harassed me for money, she was contrary, uncooperative, pig-ignorant, theatrically sour and hateful, intolerant, insincere and selfish. Before our final escape, she behaved as though I was her property or pet, and thought it natural to employ blackmail and threats in maintenance of such, as and whenever necessary. She had the lesbian barber from her inner circle shave me daily with a straight razor to remedy the stubble rash which she complained of bitterly. She sat there gesturing to areas of my face that she wanted special attention paid to with the blade. One evening I was pulling on her tits and bothering her moistened cunt with my knee, and then we started to grind and press our groins together and pull off some of our clothes. I was hard but let it only slide about underneath as I didn't have a condom and even just the sliding about was causing me concern, but she tried to goad and guide me in with her best efforts. I started to want it and suddenly the head of my cock was right there in the lips of her mess. I pulled out and off and away, breathing heavily, and she started quietly sobbing.

It was never what I wanted. I wasn't pretending otherwise to Pod. What I had to work with was slim enough already. I just need a certain degree of comfort. He was lost in the spartan simplicity of his rituals. I was trying to dig out some secret, or assemble the valuable fragments I hoped to tease out of prostitution, poverty, criminality, oriental religion, warfare and genocide and other categories. Pod and I used to talk to each other in a language that was made of slums and sex, a language that has now stagnated. I cared more about the metaphysics of prostitution than he did. In our greatest undertakings that language seemed rich, overladen almost, with meaning – it ran right through the heart of life. Whatever that meaning was or was supposed to be, the language itself has failed, folded, and sometimes I can't even find my precious and simple cruelties in its phrases. I suspect with disappointment that really all I have, the only seed sprouted, is this puerile anecdote.

—This is beautiful.

—It's a sash, see? There's one each for your mother and father.

—Is this gold?

—No. But I know you like this saint, so I had this sealed into an amulet case for you.

—It smells good. It smells of sandalwood paste. You must have paid a monk to activate it?

—(Smiles) And these, are some good pieces of cloth. You can keep them, or distribute them as you like. These are handmade, from home.

—It's too much, you've gone too far. I don't have room for it all. They are beautiful though.

—Take this stone. This is important. I won't hear argument.

—This is expensive. It's too much.

—I won't hear argument. You don't want to make me angry do you? Take it, and keep it with you. You can have it sealed on a chain if you want, that would be good.

—It's too much.

—(Raises finger) Keep it with you, on your person, ok?

Here. These aren't to be opened now.

—What are these? It better not be money. It feels like money.

—It's not. It's letters. Not to be opened now.

—Can I open them tonight before I go to the airport?

—As you wish. (Sheds tears)

—I love you. I care about you. (Tears)

—I love you my child.

—I'll be away for a long time.

—Whatever will happen will happen. I'm strong. I'm a strong woman. But you, take care of yourself.

—Where did you get these envelopes? They are beautiful.

—Oh, and there's this, I forgot.

—Please, I don't want it, it's too much. But can I take some photographs of your naked breasts?

—Yes, but don't show anyone else.

—I promise I won't. Will you sit up a little?

—Like this?

—Yes.

Nah Tee Tong was a dilapidated, faux-Greco-Roman apartment block with a swimming pool near the Arun Amarin intersection, a ten minute walk, depending on the heat and traffic, from the stifling cell I inhabited during the Second Bangkok Era. Non-residents could pay seventy baht to use the pool, which was more or less deserted during the day when it absorbed so much heat from the sun that swimming was often desperately uncomfortable.

At a certain hour, the sun passed behind another dark Pinklao tower, which became a back-lit, carbon totem in the centre of the cloudless azure. The quality of light that this produced, which can only be seen in the Asian tropics, is perfectly replicated here in the north when the sun retreats behind the peak of the mountain. I entered the swimming pool area through the gate on the soi and paid my money to the booth-girl, who slid a small ticket printed on paper as thin as bible-leaf across the counter without looking away from her little television. I put the ticket in my shirt pocket and smiled at her ear, and the profile view of her snub nose, her small, pert, salty tits in their blouse and market-bought, padded bra and her thin arms and thickly padded fingers, and I considered what it would be to know all of her and to feel her body cling to mine like a monkey, as I always and can't help doing when I see her, and then I walked through the peeling white portico, under the creepers and cracked wall tiles, up the stairs and into the pool-side area where I shed my trousers and linen shirt onto a plastic chaise longue, and felt currents of pleasure and gratitude for the intensity of the heat and the absence of people. I could hear some clucking female conversation on the upper restaurant level, and in the corner of my eye, caught the movement of starlings on the mass of electrical wiring over the portico. I raised my arms into the air and a joyous stretch reverberated out of me.

Abruptly, a shriek rang out from the restaurant level and bounced off the tower block opposite, and as I turned my head to look up I noticed a small child drowning in the pool. Her body was suspended vertically in the water with her face upturned and eyes closed like a fist just below the surface. Her mouth was open and pumping vacantly like the filter in a tank, but the water above her barely rippled. She must have been under for many minutes. I swiftly lowered myself into the hot water and reached her in two strokes, pulling her sluggish body in its blue swimsuit to my side and using my free arm to propel us back to the edge. We were in the deep end and it was difficult. The screaming woman was still on the restaurant balcony above us as far as I could tell, and there was no one else; booth-girl was not in evidence.

In the water at the edge of the pool, wondrous at the tactile intimacy we had assumed, I tried to push her up, over and out, onto the concrete ledge. But the heavy water wanted to keep her, and I worried absurdly about tearing her skin on the stone. I reluctantly let her go and pulled myself out, feeling the baked concrete sizzle under my wet arms and knees. I kneeled, tensed myself, and drew her effortlessly with one hand from the water. She emerged like an eel, sleek and beautiful, a little Siamese Princess with plump cheeks and thin arms. I laid her small body on the concrete, keeping her thighs and shoulders supported with my hands, staring into her unmoving face. She's dead I thought. The screaming woman was in my vision now but was doing nothing further. For some seconds I couldn't think what to do. Through the heat and the wet stone, my screaming witness, the miles of foreign blue above me, the ruined temple of the pool with its columns and weeds, the crude peeling statue of Venus that gestured over our tableaux with her empty eyes and broken fingers, I saw in my heart the kiss I would have to offer the little thing in front of me. Then I perceived the gravity, the weight of the pressure that was shutting her lungs, and cradled her tiny trunk, feeling the pin-prick of her child's nipple beneath the blue Lycra against my palm. I saw the little bud blossom into the full nipple of a young woman, smiling and alive, beautiful in her wretchedness like the girl in the booth, adapted to her hot, predetermined life, her bodily functions tied to agriculture, her father's pride and protective instincts fully engaged as her courtships ensue, like they were when she learned to walk and talk. Her chest was hard and brittle like carved wood, or a tortoise shell. I pushed down on it brutally, and then a second time with one hand over the other, and lo, the pressure was released in a watery orgasm of chlorine and Mama noodles that reeked of pork stock and vomit. She was alive, and the animation denied to her in the previous minutes burst furiously forward to catch up with the present moment. She flailed and moaned with resistant energy, choking and wriggling, and bits of vile noodle slithered from her nose and mouth making me gag. I stood myself up and turned on the hose coiled before the entrance to the changing rooms, rinsed the vomit from my arms and face and then from the flapping Siamese eel in its puddle of mess, nodding in relief to the noisy useless cunt who had screamed her way through my marriage to the little Princess. Another adult appeared, sombre and concerned, and I nodded and walked with a silly manly gait through the white arches into the changing rooms.

Inside the rooms, which were chambers (I think of them and call them chambers), a double row of benches was arranged down the length of the space, dividing the dusty, unused wall-lockers from the shower cubicles on the other side. The cubicles were separate, tiled rooms in their own right, with a window slit high up above one's head that faced the pool area and was glazed with thick, tinted glass. Below these, each cubicle had a showerhead fixture that was operated by a stiff metal dial adhered to the tiled wall underneath it, way down, knee-height from the floor. The lotus-bud showerheads were of a design that facilitated the adjustment of the head's angle, but in all the cubicles the heads were sealed in rust and could not be adjusted. They were all locked into different angles, some relatively extreme, which implied that the flow of water would be at an obtuse angle, and not be convenient for washing. This wasn't however the case: each showerhead, when its dial was turned fully open, issued only dribbling rivulets of yellowish water that occasionally coughed and sputtered, and thus was completely unaffected in practical terms by the angle of the showerheads. One needed to press one's body romantically against the slimy tiles to get wet. I liked the heads a great deal, and felt that they possessed their own special aesthetic in this regard. The perfect alignment and symmetry of their distribution along the wall was offset by the variance in their respective angles, an effect that was itself given yet another fresh layer of order by the identical manner in which water issued from each head regardless of its angle. To perceive this composition, one required a thorough knowledge of each and all of the cubicles and their showerheads.

The beauty of the cubicles was further enhanced by the relationship that existed between the rashes of green and brown algae, and the deep cracks in the walls. (Like many buildings in this part of the city, Nah Tee Tong had been condemned due to subsidence years before, to little practical effect. The city of Bangkok is sinking down into the swamp upon which it is built. When I last returned to Nah Tee Tong, after moving from the district, I found the crumbling pool area shut and the pool drained. Someone had thrown themselves from the top floor and been smashed apart by the poolside concrete, and the building's owner feared a wrathful ghost.) Each cubicle smelled strongly of urine, as it was convenient to urinate into the wide drain-holes directly beneath each showerhead; drain-holes which occasionally were passages for obscene animals, including once a snake which was executed and eaten by booth-girl's father and some fat women upstairs.

My fantasies and daydreams in the cubicles were often informed by the showerheads, which were awarded the bold, fascist beauty of Rome and its statuary by the faux-classical exterior of the poolside area. The showerheads were as a row of such statues – nude, black argonauts between fluted, Corinthian columns, captured in strained muscular attitudes, one bearing a discus, another gesturing earthward with a sword, a third crooked under the weight of a huge sphere. I cannot at this time remember how many showerheads there were. Not as many as six, which would certainly have been too many. More than two. Two would have been remarkable though. If there had been only two, I'd have liked it if there weren't any cubicles at all to contain them, just the tiled walls, to frame them. To bear them. Three, of course, would have been genius. Of course that number certainly would require the cubicles to cloister them. Three showerheads would have been the most suggestive of execution, of hanging bodies. But three would almost have been too perfect – the room would be less provocative with only three, and would have implied a verticality that was dishonest to its constitution, for the room was profoundly horizontal in aspect. Four is my guess, I think there were four heads, four cubicles. That is in any case by far the most harmonious number. The variance of angles to which the faces of the heads were turned was given a harmony by their distribution and symmetry, like the equally spaced strings of a guitar reverberating different notes in a chord of music. And four is the number most endowed to hold the shower-heads in that harmony, firmly and gracefully. Four removes the possibility of one standing out, regardless of how dramatic and contorted an angle a head might be turned in. This number also removes the theatrical onus placed by implication upon the bather. Four is not a number to prostrate oneself to, or be framed and flanked by. The room should be enjoyed passively without introspection or recourse to oneself. There should be no one locus of devotion.

But one, one showerhead alone on the wall, that really would surpass everything and be something else entirely. Think of it. Of course no cubicle, just the bare tiles and the head, and I should like the dial to be turned open permanently, to be frozen into its open attitude with flaky rust. I've just realised that the saffron hue of the water in those chambers was probably a consequence of the rust. One sole showerhead, with its network of warm, dribbling rivulets running and sweating over the tiles, permanently, in the subterranean chamber, where bathers would gather in line to press their bodies against the moisture one after the other. It makes me think of the cold fresh water that runs over sharp rocks on parts of this very mountain. I've pressed my unclothed body against them in like fashion.

I leaned against the tiles in my cubicle and pissed into the hole as the water from the showerhead ran and dribbled over me, and then I sank onto the cool floor with one arm under my head and my knees up. The sputtering yellow fountain made me think of tobacco, whose colour it shared. I had left my cell without my tobacco because I'd not foreseen the Day of the Siamese Eel, and do not usually smoke during those hours of the afternoon. I put the episode back together in my conscious mind. Her nipple under my palm, which I now believe I imagined, and the unyielding hardness of her trunk, inflated and watertight like a wooden bottle, the screaming harridan, the gratitude and worship owed to me that I was already composing my acknowledgement of, and the way I had been cheated by her survival. I allowed the yellow water to run down my face in recognition of my merit. She should have died, and I should have been permitted to hold her little dead body and lay her in the arms of a weeping father, and though I would also have been crying, the most replete glory would have been in the weeks following the Day of the Siamese Eel, through which I would have reared like grief rampant.

I emerged from the chambers. The Princess sat blankly on the concrete with the harridan, who said stiffly – Thank you for helping the child. I delivered my acknowledgement and slipped once again into the water and began to swim up and down, counting the lengths as I went:

The first length – The Eel and family revere me and become deeply invested in my advancement. They don't give me money, but use their patronage connections to disappear my various residency issues. As The Eel gradually comes of age, her parents gently suggest her transferral to my household, which I decline with her best interests at heart. Disappointed, they soon become comfortable with my status as Revered Uncle, and the family and I retain strong ties over the decades and throughout my various triumphs.

The second and third – The little Princess has suffered horrible brain damage. She never learns to speak properly, pisses and shits herself like a baby and needs to be spoon-fed for the rest of her life. She will only eat Mama noodles, which she smells of permanently, and which crawl from every opening in her body. Even her tear ducts emit rich, brown pork-stock tears, and the noodles slither constantly from her nose and ears. Her body itself becomes deformed and stunted, and she is confined to a series of special chairs, which I photograph in antique sepia, frame and hang symmetrically under each showerhead in the cubicles. I am invited to participate in her care, partly as an expedient measure, for the family are poor, and more than a few of them cannot help but resent my actions, both for their lack of total success and failure alike.

The fourth and fifth length – The Eel perishes, in response to my brutalising efforts. The Oriental eyes of the law are blind to all but the end result of my act. The Great White Swimmer was the last person to touch the little darling before her death. I am plunged into prison, with a kiddie-rape beef slapped on for good measure, and suspect photos of me with my hands on the dead child, taken from the restaurant balcony, appear on front pages across the country in lurid colour. The cops find traces of my semen in all of the cubicles. Other sex murders are blamed on me. My Contacts List is dissected and every two-bit hooker in Bangkok I've ever rubbed up against denounces me to friendly policemen with cash presents. It learnt to speak Siamese to further its immoral ends. I'm in general population of course, sleeping with fifty other men in a boiling, windowless basement. I kill many attackers over the years, cover myself in tattoos, and am forgotten outside the prison until I am stabbed to death with plastic blades in a shower cubicle after stealing a quadrant of papaya from another lifer.

The sixth to twenty-first lengths – You can see now, the process in which I score narratives onto that little wooden trunk, perhaps starting underneath the tiny nipple and writing around and around it in concentric circles. The child survives thanks to my intervention, and blooms like a rosebud on the temperate mountain, into a prostitute, an abject streetwalker, a whore from a slum just like Noi. I lay out again in my mind The Tale of Noi, and though it will be drawn from journal entries, notes and reveries from work logs and field notebooks, I want to say that it is not an ethnography, nor is Noi an Everywhore. The first half the Tale will be about my cruel arrogance, and the second half, my brilliant compassion and the sympathy I deserve.

THE TALE OF NOI: OR, MY FAILURE

On the right hand side of the third floor, orange neon frames two entrances with gargoyles on stools, black curtains over the entrances. The gargoyles croon at you but there is less of the hustle of the lower floors, where naked gargoyles wrench hands and sleeves and scream shrill curses at each other, because the bar dominates an entire half of the third floor, and those who climb up there obviously mean to enter. The curtained entrances look over the stone balustrade, giving a view of the path just taken from the ground. You can see the dwarf in the top hat at the entrance to the Plaza, the ground bars packed with screaming bikinis, the multi-coloured neon and billowing curtains of the first floor, with the girl's dining area to the right flank and the beauty and nail section to the left. And the second floor, swaggering she-males with theatrical sneers and hysterical gargoyles, fighting over the copious, placid bison and the bacon across their thick backs. The bars on the second floor are small and numerous, and their competition makes it the Plaza's desperate heart, a typhoon of noise and chaos. And then up here, the ladyboy clubs on the right, the private rooms and the orange neon, and the two curtained entrances of this place.

A naked girl will pull the curtain back as you approach, the gargoyles moving in behind to stroke your shoulders, and you can stop in the threshold to survey the interior before committing, as you are expected to do, and as old hand etiquette demands. A rodeo machine dominates the centre of the left hand side of the room. The bull itself is mounted over a red, air-cushioned pit, ranged with thin lengths of table for bottles and ashtrays, stools bolted to the rim. A midget sits at a control panel and operates the bull in two modes: hooker mode – bull gently rotates and dips to showboat hooker and make it look easy; bison-mode – start slow and speed up until subject is thrown from the bull within a minute. If survive beyond a minute, in theory, is given a free beer.

The apparatus functions like that. Johnny's tattoos and huge, soft cock and heroin tolerance. We take him like our mascot for the first time, winkled out from the ripe coffin of his Kao San cell; before we even arrive he asks for a few banknotes to pay something to lick and suck off his big, limp dick behind a van in the street with another ecology of creatures slithering past and forth and engines growling and farting hot, ruined air – we pay the banknotes to the painted embarrassment in question, gladly, happily for Johnny. Inside the Plaza, he chooses an elfin, waffle-eared freak of a go-go before I can show him the apparatus and explain how it works. Its spiky, long arms are like feelers of brown rusk. Gaptooth, bony buttocked, shrunken inverted nipples, big thick flat crusty flaking veiny feet, wrapped up like a junkie gift for big-nob Johnny in a black string bikini stretched over its horrible, lanky frame. I try to distract Johnny with an explanation of the apparatus. He wants his girl though, so I get old hand pleasure in blowing crisp Siamese for him into its big fungus ear. Between Johnny and it, I liquify into a gesture: an attitude of sensual authority, a heart and a brain with veins wrapped like roots all around them and with the face and hair of an English James Dean set in a laureled coat of arms in the air. It thinks *I* want it, that *I* am the john, it misunderstands. I point to Johnny. He sits with his legs wide apart and elbows lent on the rim of the slim table behind him, his big hands and manly fingers disagreeing with his teenage cut-off jeans. He smiles and leers at her with arched eyebrows.

Fuck Johnny, I thought, and plunged back into the mass of bodies in a wash of choleric irritation that faded as I lit my thirtieth cigarette of the day. Through the dry ice and noise, in the heart of a plume of cobalt steam, I saw Noi on the apparatus like Christ crucified, her large wobbly breasts under a film of northeastern sweat.

A few nights later, I returned and picked her up. In my room it was dark and unpleasant and the charge was long gone. She smelt tangy and unwashed. As she undressed, the liquid oak I had admired in the Plaza loosened and stretched. Her nipple was like a little sour olive, about to shrivel, blacken, and fall from the breast as a rotten seed-case falls from a twig, to be swept in dismissal under a table and out of sight. I juggered underneath her and stroked her damp skin and soft body and came without sensation, the cum watery and translucent. I can't remember if I kicked her out with taxi fare that night or in the morning.

I immediately forgot about Noi, though I did vaguely notice her in the pit again some weeks later, her image turned to meat and absolutely devoid of any meaning or interest. I continued along my sewer tunnels in the usual obnoxious fashion. Then one morning there was a knock at my door. It was Noi. The scumbag peers tell you that all whores are hyenas with no exception, and the very silence and blankness of her expression appeared to me then to signify the sullen malice of a hustler's revenge. I asked her what the fuck she thought she was doing, and angrily pointed out that my wife could well have been in here for all she knew. No, she said, she had been downstairs since yesterday to make sure that wasn't the case. My fear crystallised, and I dismissed her with cruel words spoken at high volume, then closed the door with a controlled authority and stood still behind it for a few seconds as my blood raced. I looked through the peephole and she was gone.

A full year later, with Pod gone home and Johnny in prison, temporarily homeless and inebriated, I made an uneasy and foul-tempered progress into the public toilet behind the petrol station at the Plaza intersection. I remember seeing that fucking dwarf in his top hat who always replied to my Siamese in English, and deciding to invent an elaborate story about receiving a blowjob from him, to release into the gossip of the bars like a malicious fart. A hooker was lingering in the toilet but I was way beyond sober piss-fear. When I was finished I turned to find her dark eyes focused right on me. What the fuck are you looking at, I slurred. In the silence her face gradually collected together under my wavering vision, and I saw that it was Noi. She wore a cheap shirt and shorts, red plastic shoes and a blank expression.

We walked to an expensive, by-the-hour hotel across the street and I hungrily mauled her breasts as she removed our respective amulets and covered them prudently and discreetly with a flannel on the side-table. I pulled off my watch and kicked off my trousers and lovingly fucked her from on top while kissing her open mouth. My fuck was like a Howitzer. I was completely remade, and whilst falling asleep I was clearly aware in myself that I would react without any regret or resentment if I awoke to find my wallet light or missing. I almost welcomed the moral poetry of the possibility.

I awoke that afternoon in a pleasant, alcoholic fug, and suggested to Noi that we step out for a meal. I fucked her again as she dressed herself with the same intensity as before. The sky outside was that piercing, monsoon silver-grey that makes your eyes water and your armpits start to drip from the heat. We climbed down some wonderful passageways of blackened concrete that led to the canal and bought two fetid mackerels and a bag of rice from some old crone. The mackerels came with mashed chilli, and the crone gave us a beaker of water. I asked Noi questions while we dined on this compost, and she gave me straightforward and uncomplicated answers. She had a room on the ground floor of an unfinished building in a small slum alley off Arun Amarin. We boarded the first boat that came after the meal was finished, and I gave her my arm as the solid ground fell away from us.

I'd walked past her little pocket of slum a number of times. A gap in a wall led to an elevated concrete walkway over a stagnant pond of black sewage and a mess of jagged iron girders. The aspect of the unfinished building on the other side was like an artificial cliff-face, punctuated with tiny balconies and breathing holes. Stalls, residents and dogs collected around three august and doorless entrances to the vertical slum. I bought a pineapple from a young man on the way inside, and suffered a flush of embarrassment at Noi's sudden and curt instruction to formally yield my respect to a statuette of Mae Torani in a grotto cluttered with burnt down incense sticks and yellow candle wax. Her room was third on the left, and I completed the decision to move in when I saw it had a door with a working padlock hoop.

It was at this stage in that I developed my routine of loosing vulnerable green roots that snaked their way outside and over the slim walkway, toward Nah Tee Tong, where I pursued my Doric fixations with the showerheads in the odorous tiled chambers, and swam through the hot oil from which I drew out the little Siamese Eel. My life seems in retrospect to have run like canal water through these paths that I scored daily through the grids of slum, the furious roads and traffic gardens with their painted, concrete animal sculptures, and the tiles and cubicles, rather than inside my watery sperm, or Noi's ruined womb, or her soft tits. And not the melancholy absence that was constantly a part of her kindness and obedience, her weird understanding, her very female resilience and loneliness. Have a look at these picture-postcards of our life together:

—The card shows a black-and-white photo of Noi and I sitting on the pallet in our room. The dusty plastic fan hides our bodies but you can see our faces which wear queer expressions. The expressions are due to the fact that we are watching a small, richly patterned frog climb the adjacent wall, which is visible in the lower left-hand corner of the postcard.

—The card shows me posing in front of the open door of the communal toilet. My pride in the toilet is in evidence. I am dressed in a Burmese sarong and lightly dusted with turmeric, and wearing a broad, happy smile. The rotten wood of the door has long, rusty nails hammered into it. The toilet interior is dark, but you can make out that the toilet is a squatter not a sitter.

—The card shows a close-up photo of my face focused in concentration, though you can tell

I have just woken up. I am straining to listen to an unpleasant conversation between Noi and the headman of the slum just outside our door. He is extorting extra rent from her with the assumption that it can and will come out of my farang pocket. And it does.

—The card shows a photograph taken with the flash of us sleeping in the darkness. Noi is curled like a cat on the pallet and I am spread out supine on a blanket on the concrete floor, my head resting on my rolled-up trousers. Alarmingly, there are several large cockroaches on the ground around me.

—The card shows a photo of Noi squatting over the communal toilet. It is taken from behind and slightly above her, showing her upper back and the back of her pretty head, her arms spread out and her hands touching the walls either side of her to steady herself, but you wouldn't know this because the photo cuts off the arms above the elbow at each side, as in a Byzantine crucifixion icon.

—The card shows a colour photo of Noi rubbing balms into my back, which is covered in tiny red spots in two broad stripes that concentrate respectively over the shoulder blades. I used to call this slum-rash. It seems to occur temporarily in reaction to excessive levels of dirt and sweat.

—The card shows a picture of us picking apart and eating a sun-dried fish. I remember the occasion well, the fish was small, but salty and delicious. I crunched up even the harder bones and swallowed them for the calcium.

—The card is a photographic montage of our toi-let-kit. I see no virtue in describing the layout, so will simply list the items depicted: a plastic cup containing toothpaste and our two tooth-brushes; a worn down piece of Protex soap; a lump of alum, which can be used as an effective underarm deodorant for life, leaving no yellow patches or crust on clothing and costing about five baht per lump; a bottle of woman's sham-poo and conditioner; a small but charming collection of balms and fragrant oils with co-lourful and sometimes bizarre labels; a straight razor in a plastic case, with a packet of carefully wrapped spare blades.

—The card shows a photograph of Noi and I in the small lean-to restaurant, watching the por-table television with our plates scraped clean in front of us.

Noi and I are beautifully composed and arranged in our concrete cell, graceful and iconic in the shapes of our languor, effortlessly capturing the pathos and ideal-ism in our union. Listen:

—I'm an unusual choice for you am I not?

—Yes, you're young.

—My body is young. Do you love this place more than me?

—I don't know. I took you and followed you before we came back here.

—Back here? Do you think older women are easier to trust?

—As a general rule, yes. What criteria do you employ to judge our sincerity?

—I don't. The mysteries and complexities of causation and chance do not require more than instinct on my part. But we rely on our patrons, and we aren't so meek as to veil our desires from them.

—I think we labour under our own set of illusions. Do we seem like non-humans to you?

—Sometimes. But that's not really the way I think. Everything is because of another thing. You seem foolish to us when you act as though that were not the case. It's not philosophy, there's only the natural truth. You are the masters of philosophy, which is a harmful distraction. To ask questions you know cannot be answered is foolish.

—But we are rich.

—That's not really true, as you know.

—I know.

—It's a young girl's illusion that doesn't take long to shake off.

—That's true. Why do you still ask me for money?

—You know why. Is it so displeasing to you that the surroundings of instances of moral beauty should reflect that beauty through their own qualities and therefore be in unity?

—And you love your mother?

—I understand gratitude as a social currency. (If it wasn't for my mother I wouldn't have these breasts that you love to chew and wet with your spit.)

—Is it as romantically desperate as it seems?

—You'll never know.

—How do you imagine your own sadness for yourself?

—It is a sensational phenomenon, not an oil painting.

—But there must be an emblem you can refer to.

—I told you, that is a European disease. Look up at that shelf there by the ceiling.

—Yes.

—I've no need to paint my environment. I'm as secure as one can expect to be. Do you think your security is increased by artfully misunderstanding your environment as a remedy for the absence of the thrills of crime?

—I've never thought of it as security. I try very hard to be sincere, when I doubt myself or suspect my own motivation, when I spot weak or rotten roots I pull them out quite ruthlessly. I am ruthlessly honest with myself and the subjects that concern me, my pride and my instinct dictate it.

—You are not so different from others in my experience. But you eat rice and speak the Bangkok tongue, and you were among my first.

—I hate the heroes and the libertines. I just want to belong where I am. I am being honest.

—You can belong to me. You can save me and fuck me.

—I can't save you, no one can. And soon I probably won't fuck you anymore. I can't separate guilt and pity out from love, ever. When we fuck I cling to your body and I love it, but I can feel the cruelty flowing through me.

—Next month some and friends and I will go to Chiang Rai and work in an orchard collecting fruit for a month or so.

—I know you see evil in nature. You know, if you died I would love you more. I would worship your flat image, and my reverence wouldn't fade but rather increase. You should die, and be risen up high. Don't you have any fondness for this place?

—I do not. Can't you separate me from this place?

—I think so. I try very, very hard to do that constantly, but in those efforts I usually end up making of you another place.

—Tell me what you know about agriculture.

—I do find it sacred, when it's *inside you*. People and places stack up inside each other. I've never lived in or visited a Bangkok slum that was not Isan. I'm not saying they don't exist. I want to talk about generalisations again. Can we do that?

—You have to be careful.

—I am jealous of prostitutes. I want to be near them because I wish I were as abject as I assume they are. I want to write a novel called WHORE that is told in the first person from a prostitute's perspective. Prostitutes are the easiest and most accessible source of abjection and suffering, which is harder to touch than you think. I can both share in it with them and cause them to feel it through easy, selfish acts that are hardly premeditated.

—These are not your formulations. They are not your attitudes, they are a facade. Tell me what a prostitute is. Is a prostitute an idea or just another human being?

—Is money the only reason you moved to the city? Do you feel supported by the other Isan people that live here? Do you help each other? Do you love your mother? Did your mother cuddle you when you were young, and now? Was it her who raised you? Are you physically affectionate, the two of you? Does she give you motherly advice? And finally, how much does she know, and to what extent is she responsible?

—You haven't breathed into me enough. You never breathe deeply enough.

—Is your life better with me?

—Yes.

—Am I the same as your flat images up there?

—You're a product of them.

—Like a piece of fruit?

—How do you love me differently?

—I want to get close to you the way a monk tries to get close to a corpse.

—You want to rub your face with soil from my birthplace? You need to relate sexually to agriculture? To grasses and trees?

—I want to ask you about your father's absence and what role it plays in your religious repertoires.

—There is no religion. You become tedious to me again. There are patrons and there are traditions. Do you love me?

—I want you to rise up and be illuminated as the perfect Isan whore.

—Where will you take me? Where do I belong?

—You belong here.

—I feel the potential of cruelty in you. I feel it charged all over and through your body, your belly ripples with it, your eye shimmers with it.

—I was, back near the beginning, very keen, very desperate, to hurt somebody. But fear is insidious, it lingers into indecision, corrodes resolve.

—How does cruelty relate to me? And to women who work hard?

—They are linked in my mind. I'm looking for the gentleness of Christ in you – Christ the mother.

—Prostitution is your destiny, your prison. It did not

seduce you. You have worked towards it.

—David hung himself in the disabled cubicle of the Justinlees on his birthday. They didn't find him the next day because the lazy cleaner couldn't be bothered to open the stuck door of the cubicle. Davie's cubicle. His father, a janitor, arrived at the pub the next day looking for the birthday boy literally minutes after they found the hanging corpse. And everyone was mystified because there was no reason. I've locked myself into that cubicle, I've smelt the piss there, breathed it in hundreds of times. I've drunk hundreds of pints of beer and whisky in that pub and pissed it mostly into that same cubicle, because I don't like the public trough. I don't like the public. I liked Davie's cubicle.

—Is all sex really just violence?

—No. I don't think so. And my pain will always be subservient to yours, or any Asian's.

I am finding increasingly as time passes that decisions are being made for me, on my behalf, by an agency I attribute to my impressions of the environment itself. I feel I'm being slowly gathered up by the fibres and essences of the forest, beckoned and cajoled by leaves and scents, and chased by plagues sent to precede me and to show me the way. My own face looks down on me from the trunks of these dark trees, the moist branches I grab are my own sweaty cock and the fluids that splash on me are my own issue. Hair and skin and waste from my body are here forever now and parts of my history and development are firmly entwined in the paths I've cut and re-cut. I've dropped stones and strips of coconut husk into stagnant water that will resonate with consequence throughout these mountains, and fertilised glades with my shit and saliva. Where else would I ever celebrate myself again?

A dense smoky haze hangs in the air. I am lost in the smell as I sweep the leaves and dust from my veranda and wince as I suddenly notice my neighbour's purple-toothed grin, camouflaged amongst the leaves and shrubs beneath me. There is a poisonous toad in her fish tank and she would like my assistance in removing it.

Her house is smaller and more elegantly built than the lodge, its interior filled with statuettes and idols, the air fragrant with jasmine and small bowls of scented water. I scoop the toad up, out of the tank and it sighs as I toss it into the whispering dusk. A grin splits her face open again in gratitude, each purple tooth engorged, her eyes and nostrils sealing over as they stretch back around her skull which is not made of bone, but flexible cartilage. Her northern dialect is chipped, as if the words and phrases are being cut into chunks of wood with a hammer and chisel, the characters small and rustic, but precise. She points through the darkness to some tiny wisps of light across the ravine, through the trees, somewhere beyond the corrugated iron shacks of the Lisu settlement. Fire. I'm tired and unconcerned. I decline her offer of refreshments with thanks and walk back to the lodge, which is situated at the very furthest and highest reach of the orchard, on the swell of the mountain, five meters from the dilapidated barbed-wire fence that borders the mountain proper. I feel the depths of mud and rock and the ocean of trees above as I lay myself down.

I awake in a panic from unpleasant dreams, with a bursting bladder and an iron hard-on. There is something wrong with me; I can't breathe properly, there are noises and lights. I swing my body up and lean against the flimsy rattan wall, cutting my hand on a splinter. Through the windows I see hissing rivers of fire. The room is full of smoke. I realise that the lodge, made as it is from parched wooden fronds, is moments from destruction. I have to fight. I push open the door and spring forth in the nude with my hard-on wobbling in front of me. There are waves of fire rolling down the thickly forested swell of the mountain, the closest has eaten its way through the carpet of dead leaves to within metres of the lodge.

I turn on the hose and let it run, take a bucket and fill it from the stone water barrel underneath the veranda and run clumsily around the building to throw the entirety at the closest advancing flames, extinguishing less than a square foot for my effort. I collect another bucketful and this time scoop the water out, over and in front of the fire with better results. Where there are only leaves, no wood or old tyres, the blaze is vulnerable and easy to resist, and soon I am able to refine my technique, extending a protective circle of water around the lodge. The urgency and adrenaline begin to dissipate together, leaving only the weight of the labour necessary to complete the task. I find my shoes and put them on. I become zealous and obsessed, hopping over the barbed wire and running precisely up the steep swell between bamboo spikes and gnarled roots, cutting strategic gaps through the fire's front lines, concentrating attacks on clumps of dead bamboo and old wood where the element has entrenched itself.

I'm done by the time my landlady Auntie Goodly gets here with hoses and bottles of Coke and sweets for everyone. Purple-tooth stands silently outside her residence, her tiny body a silhouette against the open doorway. Goodly is beside herself with motherly excitement, her booming voice echoes around the orchard asserting her leading role in the drama. At last, piss dribbles free from my semi onto the warm earth. Exhausted, filthy and naked, I stand in awe of vistas of flame illuminating distances of land and forest not normally visible through the trees.

I go back to bed in my smoky room, and fall straight asleep.

Then, outside in the daylight, there is a scream. A scream of horror from a hoarse throat, an intense and sustained scream. I awake by degrees to this sound and listen to it, feel it, as it bridges the dream I was having with my woken state, and as it gathers to itself a greater sense of intrusion and threat.

I rise and peer from the window. The scream is coming from a very large wild pig, its body twisted and its lower jaw clamped hard in the bite of a ferocious pit-bull of less than half its size. A pair of diminutive hill people stand on either side of the two animals, one holding a small knife. He sees me at the window and says something to his friend, whose eyes also dart up to my window. The screaming and the tableaux of this foursome burns itself into the cultural treasury of the lodge.

Over so many seconds, under the scrutiny of these men, I feel like an intruder. Their stretched, golden-ochre faces and black eyes are not my business, and the arrogant roots and reasons I have thrown down here without thought, without regard for black eyes and cruel dogs, come apart like wet cardboard, and I feel shame in the recognition that the lodge, the orchard and the mountain are foreign to me. And to punctuate and emphasise this point that they had come here to make, the man with the knife turns and clumsily stabs the pig in its side. The scream begins to falter as the great animal loses its balance, and the other man collects the flowing blood in a banana leaf.

I sink down weakly onto the bed, my limbs brittle, and fold into myself, my eyes sealing over. A few years ago I saw a Burmese woman who had been savagely raped and beaten by a soldier. She was crumpled up in a foetal ball like a sickly animal, nestled in the foliage. Her naked bottom and crotch were visible and her sobs had this warbling in them that made it an effort to breathe. I thought I could actually smell the blood and other fluids in the humid forest air. Have you ever smelt elephant yams in the forest? They smell like acrid rotting flesh, it makes you salivate and you can taste the smell, it's awful. At first I was just flattened by this powerful guilt, not even anything like pity, just horribly cloying guilt. It was as though in seeing the woman I had to take responsibility, as if I'd asked to see this, as if I'd paid for it. At the same time the poetry of the damaged body with its strange colours and composition made tender suggestions to me, made me yearn for femininity and all the ways it can wrap around you like water. Over the days and weeks that followed my intellectual responses became more or less abstracted, and somewhere I lost the means of measuring my own sincerity. I would listen deep down into myself for it.

The point at which I realised I didn't ever want to have conversations with western travellers again came months later, shortly before I moved to the mountain, when I told a female tourist in a bar about the experience with the Burmese woman. I was trying to be honest both for her benefit and perhaps to solicit some casual therapy, but she found me offensive, to a dangerous degree, and I immediately realised that all conversation was hopeless and deceitful. There is experience outside of language and ideas that you assume and allow for, if you're not a cunt.

In the end I cannot deny that this is who and where I am. But I want to go back again. I ride my bike out of the orchard and down into the village for petrol and rice first, then out onto the road into the city. I twist the throttle full and climb quickly into fifth gear. Dust itches my eyes and road-tears crawl up my forehead as I hit a hundred kilometres an hour. I feel the adrenaline fire through my body as I swoop around cars and pickups, no room for mistakes at this speed. I shoot like a rocket over the intersection and steadily apply the brake as the city moat comes into view, slowing down to a reasonable sixty, my heart thumping with exhilaration and relief as it always does.

I feel deep, malign anxiety as I ride past groups of dumpy hand-shandy girls. Fat marbled legs, buttocks and breasts, snouts flattened round large sensual mouths smeared in brilliant colour, calloused scoop-like mon-key-hands. I like to see them in ordinary clothes, not trash hooker outfits. The Dwarf wore a t-shirt, a tight pink t-shirt. It feels like the first times again, but there's a horrible nervous energy now that overwhelms any sexual charge. The first thing is to get properly drunk. This night and the neon used to belong to me. In my drained heart that was once full, I know that I can't return to that limited theatre, and every time I slow down I feel violence and nausea smiling up from inside me making my eyes water.

I finally park and sit down at a bar in a pavilion of open-plan bars near a sick animal in shorts and a holiday shirt with whom I disgust myself by wanting to talk. A conversation is undertaken according to etiquette; smug, bigoted observations spoken into the rim of beer bottles with long pauses and absurd nonchalance. I grind into myself with anxiety, and presently it has softened its facade somewhat and focused its full attention. It thinks I am the same as it.

I turned, choked with resentment. And looked at it in the eye. I like jungle cunt too, it spoke at me in some more or less arrangement of language. It was seeking fellowship in its piracy and the validation of its crimes. There were simply no adequate words with which to express my rebuttal. I drove toward it and elbowed its cheek, falling out of my stool and hearing a shrill female scream from the other side of the bar. Bent over in submission and clutching its face, it made a sound of outrage. Confident now of diminished risk and powered by racing adrenalin, I aimed and released a controlled assault-punch at its head with my left fist, the better fist, and it sank in full to the floor. I mounted the body lustfully to punch and bash its poor head on the ground until my rhythm gave out. I loved doing it. I can barely prevent my arms from re-enacting the movement now. Then I clutched his head like a bowling ball, fingers and thumb like a grappling claw in nostril, jaw and eye-socket, and pulled him by his face off the wooden boardwalk. I spat on him lovingly and left the bar nursing my agonised fingers and knuckles, unable to physically contain myself as the adrenalin drained suddenly out of my muscles, and retching twice before vomiting in earnest as soon as I was out of sight.

Identity is only a short or long list of acts signified by parts of the body. How much weight it carries is up to you, but it goes on forever and ever.

Nok - cunt and mouth

Lek - cunt, arse and mouth

Noi - cunt, AIDS

Nin - mouth and tits, genital warts

Or - psychotic, cunt and mouth, AIDS

Pen - cunt

Nit - not yet

Nen - cunt and arse

Nat - mouth and hand

Ot - hand and mouth

Moo - cunt only, spots

Lek 2 - mouth, cunt and arse

In - mouth and tits, tears, AIDS

Noi 2 - mouth and cunt

Eh - cunt only, free

Nat - cunt, irregular nipple

Pee - mouth and hand, operation scars

Lek 3 - hand and mouth and tits

Nan - mouth, cunt and arse

Pen 2 - everything, full-blown AIDS

Lee - reluctant mouth, cunt, Malaysia

It - mouth, brown teeth, cunt

Noo - watery cunt

Or 2 - cunt and arse

Nok 2 - mouth and cunt

Goong 2 - hand, mouth and cunt

Daeng - suspect rash, if you're in that part of town

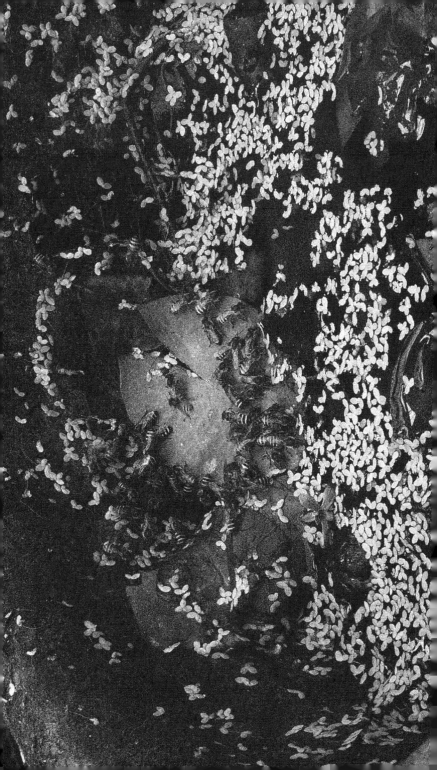

An hour later I put on my special trousers and a shirt and step out of the lodge, climbing through the ashes and ruined foliage to the fence, and follow the scorched earth up the mountain as far as it will take me. As I get higher and start to weaken and feel the different kind of anxiety that comes with roaming great distances from the lodge, the silent black slopes and lonely trunks seem more like abandoned buildings, remote, forgotten, empty and dead, and I arrange my body out flat against a patch of damp ash. The air is humid and still and the ash clings to my wet skin, turning it the colour of charcoal.

Further up I find a clearing of hill people shrines. Their bird-like paper deities are hanging from bamboo staffs arranged in circles around rattan tables of offerings. Plastic swords and knives are piled under the tables, which are covered with food. On a freshly cut tree stump sits a single pineapple, and near it are some banana leaves splashed with fresh blood. Nearby I see a more unusual arrangement: two short sticks stuck into the earth with long feathers stuck into notches. Between the sticks is a small hole gouged into the ground containing the organs of some animal, and the whole arrangement is splattered with fresh blood, only just starting to coagulate. I climb further still, concentrating on my legs, the burning pressure on my knees and ankles, the muscles in my calves and thighs. I climb myself into a deep and weary solitude, and fall asleep in a dry treeless oasis where the heat of the sun is soothing and warm, and the birdsong covers me over like a blanket.

I sleep for hours, waking after a melancholic dream. In the dream, my penis had grown into a tree, each vein and lump sprouting and growing into branches and boughs from which leaves blossom, and I pick the leaves at random and see the shapes I love written on them. As I climb the tree I almost forget there is a top, and am horrified to suddenly feel the great wooden ridges of my helmet. I had also forgotten my urethra. The artery gapes wide like the mouth of a well, the bloated lips cracked and worn. Inside is a bottomless black cylinder, smelling of warped, rotten wood and petrified fish. I am not inclined to climb back down.

I walk on, like Scott.

The anxiety and foreboding in my heart is confused by moments of rapture that are caused by sunlight. In these moments, I feel the vastness of the sky above me move gracefully and deliberately, although its face is hidden by the wooden columns and canopies, and then powerful rays of light split open tunnels of horizontal space that cut right through the verticality with vivid passages of detail. And I can tell you that the light, it unlocks such perfumes, and such sensations of enveloped memory, which unfold so potently like flowers of song in the mind, matured in the dark, marinated in the deep, rank meat of the brain for so long they seem as to be impressions of another life, and so fear is instantly cut through with longing, and the most intense rapture.

Apart from the sun, two other elevated presences assert themselves at intervals through the veiled pillars of air. Meet them: they are water and the Legume tree. Would you like to drink and bathe in cool running mountain water as it babbles and flutters around you in unbroken whispers? I'll cleanse my hands carefully, then reach into the clear water and scoop out handfuls of black tadpoles to swallow. Don't chew, they're sour. And the sharp wet rocks are an excruciating tonic.

Legumes are as monumental and still as the water will run forever. Their heart-shaped leaves strike at the mountain's unity through the impression of foreign purpose in their design. In the forest they are whales among fish, with dimpled skin covering their massive, angular shanks of plate bone. Their lives span entire human ages. Certainly it's true that many beautiful birds can be seen in their branches: the *Superb Fruit Dove*, the *Wompoo Fruit Dove*, the *Pink-spotted Fruit Dove*, the *Ornate Fruit Dove*, the *Orange-bellied Fruit Dove*, all of which I have watched squabbling over the tree's tiny fruit, as well as the *Torresian Imperial Pigeon* and even the *Purple-tailed Imperial Pigeon*.

I am delivered now like a child. The columns of my chameleon oubliette thin out suddenly into rough earthen basins that surround a triad of Legumes. I've never seen trees so big or frightening. My heart is pounding and I can't go any nearer. I stare up at the giants, hypnotised. It becomes cold. The warmth has gone also from the light. A mist begins to uncurl itself downward from the titanic limbs, unfurling out glacially into dramatic shapes like the long hair of a woman's corpse in water. I hear the patter of raindrops on the leaves before a grape-sized droplet explodes on my forehead, and I get just a flutter of the water's essence – it smells of earth and hard, flat stones. The rain comes in earnest at the same point as the mist seals its shimmering veil through the air.

The great winged trunks of the Legumes form alcoves of shadowy silver. The one in front of me offers itself through the mist like the entrance to a Cistercian monastery. The giant is beyond weight, beyond measure; a great ladder into the heights of empty sky, whose roots are flung down so deep through the layers of earth and rock. This it suggests to me with only the limited extent of its structure that I can look upon from this vantage, this hulking Masonic buttress, attached to a soaring and plummeting verticality that I perceive through a powerful metonym. Something vile scuttles and brushes at my side and it stirs me from worship. I cry out into the rain like Galahad, and crawl through mud and thorns toward the Alcove.

I'm crying. The tree permits me to tear open and remove my shirt and trousers. The pockets are empty and I own nothing. I discard the clothes in a voluptuous gesture. The rain flagellates my bare body. I stretch out my arms and press my whole body into mud and plant matter and long to be comfortably deep inside it. I wrestle the mud and clutch at it and myself and smear it into my face and hair but the rain washes it down. The rain recedes very slightly and this provides the urgency that fertilises my full abandon. I beat the churning mud with my arms, thrash, vomit a bit and throw my body awkwardly as I retch and try to sing. I strike a vertical pose, my head thrown back and eyes forced open, the rain lacerating the surface of my eyeballs. I dive back into the mud and am badly cut by something across my ribs. I look at the cut to see the blood but my eyes are on fire from the rain. I crawl.

I try to gouge a hole with my hands and I imagine myself in the hole with the wet mud wrapped around me. I'd be crouched and warm, my muscular arms cradling my raw face, head covered safely under a hood of mud, *inside* the mountain, inside the earth, *in harmony* with the soil. But I can't do it, it's like scratching at flowing sewage in a tunnel. I nuzzle and rub my face in the mud as a passionate apology and feel blood pump sparingly but steadily into my penis, not because of the soil or the rain, or the sensation of it on my face and eyes or in my mouth, but out of the satisfaction I derive from my virtuoso gesture of sensitive capitulation. And then there is that visceral spasm that my language has yet to capture, that draws from the liberation attained through abject behaviour, and the Great Warm Ecstasy that one feels absolutely *beside* one in these moments (do you know these moments?), like a giant bubble that could be leapt into, but only ever recedes like the object of desire in a dream. And you'll agree that my harmony is the touchstone, my attribute, and that the danger and hunger I bravely endure are real and necessary, and have qualified my ascension.

Black, nobbly growths of tree in the mist around the church of legumes need my tribute, the rain announces it by softening for ominous seconds as thunder explodes very near us in the sky, and the rain is unleashed in full again, and finally, in its unforgiving crescendo. I am the image of frailty, I have penetrated to the very centre of that image, and my genuinely damaged form shivers, it shakes, for these reasons: I am cold because the warmth has left me and I have climbed up and out of it wilfully; I have thrown away my clothes and food, and I am hungry; I am cut, scraped and pierced by the forest as it has followed me upwards, and the water that falls like sarcastic poison from the sky has beaten and ferociously whipped my body so that I am humiliated. My crimes, of which I still cannot speak other than by insinuation, have worked with the mysteries of my environment to show me a vehicle of humility. But the rain also lashes my soft, hideous buttocks to extract the last trace essences of the gravity, personal glory and honour of cruelty, which, in their evergreen cancers, are by these very words imbued with the elegance and satisfaction with which I laud them and define myself still.

I shake now, because my heart is cold. My hands and fingers grope stones and roots and slide through matter I cannot identify or understand. I think of mud, shit, rice-water, heavily corroded sandstone in nets of rubbery plant roots, buried hearts and lungs, the lean flesh of Asian limbs, soft, spongy penis-meat cut and packed like cigars, the horrific clumps of glandular matter that hide in women's breasts. I move my arms through the violence and grip the black branches and their skin gives like flesh. I lick the course shafts and cup bulbous protrusions and confusions of growth. The living wood gasps as I'm beaten and stroked, and my arms, so wet and muscular, follow my mouth dancing into obscene congress with hard, sour fingers.

My lips bleed and I'm in real agony, I retch again before the conclusion, but in giddy relief because I am in a triumph of elevation. I move my nude, tormented body now toward The Great Legume without regard for further ritual. The rain has thinned and the mountain fog is thicker than oil-smoke. The colossus emerges from it first as a terrifying shadow like a huge shark in the murky ocean, and then a cathedral of silver light with its beautiful arch of tropical-gothic inscription. Inside it I stroke the wet, elephant-skin walls of the alcove and prepare to perform the *final masturbation*. There is a curious satisfaction and necessity in failure however, for before I am able to come I fall fast asleep.

I awake naked into the sunlight, which paints the hanging creepers that are a curtain over my alcove, the thorn bushes, black trunks and banana leaves, the damp earth. Everything is absolutely still except some whining insects and the animated sapphire of a tired dragonfly. I turn and look up into the soaring heights of trees and sky above me, and though this is the highest place offered to me by the mountain, I've never felt deeper and more buried in the embrace of death. I don't feel any satisfaction in my renunciations, in fact I can find no moral meaning in any of it. It is simply movement, like the dragonfly.

And so I slowly disintegrate into the forest floor, the leaves, soil and the roots of the trees, my body pulsates and cracks open, blooming into tendrils of desiccated meat, flakes of putrid sponge and concentrated humors that run out in all directions from the centre of my heart like the light from a dying candle that is assimilated endlessly into the blackness of a cave. And the remaining image and impression of this almost perfect oblivion, the furthest I have crawled from organization, was in the dry prisms of filtered sunlight through the shoals of aching leaves that showed to me the eyes of an indifferent heaven, which they honoured with the illumination of vast spaces.

My heart opens again into the great angel of the city, wriggling through her stagnant vein, down, out, into the Klong. And the vein extends out from me, perfect and straight in the tarry black water of the Klong's dead canal, the septic spine of the slum, in a mist of oily urine vapour. The vapour moistens my eyes, I see and think from the canal, and my right arm, with its joints and sinews, reaches up into the heights of a tree, my fingers bending and dissipating in the leaves. In my left hand, on a stretch of tarpaulin that follows the vein, and is dusted with cement powder, as is everything, sit three fat, toad-like whores on plastic chairs. The pores of their skin are visible on their jowls, perforating their white face paint and they ooze droplets of sweat. Their taut trollop mouths are stained thick with red paint and fake gold hangs from their ears. Their black hair is tied in the bump and bun style of the Klong that I love, stretching their foreheads back over their scalps that I would kiss and bite, some rogue strands glued to their necks with sweat. Their eyes are sunken and clouded over out of respect for their dimpled, powdery cleavages. The powder hangs in the air around them like the vapour of the canal. I can feel my groin and thighs packed in the jellied meat of compacted soil and rock deep under the tarpaulin and the slabs of road, the mineral layers correspond to each useless joint and tendon. My lungs have been hollowed out into parasitic hovels on either side of the canal, strip bulbs and tiny televisions run off car batteries in each, and dried skeletons of old men, warped by weather and tattoos, sit cross-legged inside, drinking liquid from chipped glasses. The linings of my stomach are a coating on the sky, forming a dome over the Klong and sealing it. I gesture with all my body, find my left hand and push my face into a whore's soft flesh, asking where my heart is. The flesh turns to damp concrete in response, and I peel my face from it and stand up. I walk along the canal, through the vapour and the oily shit, over dogs and past hovels, stoop to touch the rotted, mossy wood of an impassable foot bridge, stretch out my arm and gently touch the powdered wrinkly flesh of the whores that line the canal on plastic chairs, one after another, thighs and breasts, lips and hair, hands and cheeks, until they run out, the last ones watching me as I glide on beyond them, finding my feet through the vapour as I walk towards the Hotel of the Autumn Triptych.

The walls of the canal are furnished with a luxuriant, sleek covering of aquatic moss, and are supported with thick iron buttresses a metre apart. I want to adhere my favourite photographs of women in the spaces between these buttresses, in identical frames, a foot above water level. Photographs from early magazines, the original relics themselves, not all of which I still own but I remember them constantly, and from books on pregnancy and breastfeeding and women's health, where large breasts are so rare and special. I know exactly the pictures I would choose to frame and exhibit here, they are all the figureheads of great dynasties, a long study of the most perfect forms that I worship. And if I could adhere these frames here between the buttresses on the canal walls, equally spaced, one after the other, after the last one was mounted I would sink slowly down into the warm black water in satisfaction.

The clerk sits in his booth reading a newspaper like always, and I hand him a banknote in exchange for the key to a numbered room. I walk around the booth, past the silent karaoke bar and climb the stairs to the first floor, watching the lizards hunting flies around the strip bulbs and air-holes in the bricks, as the excitement builds in my stomach. As I walk along the bare concrete corridor with green and brown water damage that I love, my feet stick on the grime, my nose fills with cement dust, insect wings tickle my neck, sweat forms a film over my forehead, my rectum tightens, my long, spongy semi-erect cock hangs, bouncing freely, from my open fly. I am following and preceding hundreds of thousands of prostitutes and men and clerks and cleaners in my passage along this corridor, cheap shirts, white pancake, fake gold, long fingernails, monkey-hands, plastic combs, condoms, keys, handbags, amulets, painkillers, skin cream, antiseptic lozenges, small strips of carbolic soap, worn thin towels, dusty telephones, unused furniture rusted shut. Flared nostrils, black eye-slits, sharp high cheekbones, chimpanzee ears, squarish jaws, soft, dimpled, speckled, aged, yellow flesh with brown forearms. Fat breasts, folds, lardy buttocks, thin shapeless legs, wrinkled neck, hanging nipples. Crow's feet. Red smiles. Giggling. Light slaps. Electric buzzing. Fatigue.

I stand in my room, lit with a bare bulb so I can read the graffiti and see my penis, and look at the sex rubbish strewn on the floor and the bed, which still has damp patches, and let my trousers and boxer shorts fall down to my ankles, and in a brief gesture, loose my silver sperm onto the bed, as I promised I would with my banknote. Laid down on the bed, tired, spread out, feeling the hot air blown against my bare legs by the fan, I'm ensconced in the hour that I alone have purchased, which came after the one which preceded it, and before the one that will follow, when someone else whom I wouldn't want to know will see the outline of my form pressed into the bed sheet.

The first confessional sex graffiti I remember reading was in a motorway services in Northern England somewhere when I was small.

> ONE DAY WHEN OUR PARENTS HAD GONE OUT ME AND MY BROTHER PUT ON SOME PORNO. I GOT HARD AND COULD SEE MY BROTHER WAS STROKING HIS HARD-ON. I REACHED OVER AND STARTED TO WANK HIM AND HE DID THE SAME FOR ME. I THOUGHT FUCK IT, AND GAVE HIM A GOB-ALL. HE DIDN'T MIND AND WHEN HE CAME HE LENT OVER AND SUCKED ME. NOW WE WANK AND SUCK ALL THE TIME.

In my primary school toilets (the room is mine forever), under the shrill and tender scents of a hundred years of piss-cured turds, naked arse on the immovable toilet seat and pen in hand, myself and every other toilet scribe, gripped by the often misguided excitement of anonymity, would write either a cock or a swastika. The cubicles were the containers of fantastic murals of annotated nazi homosexuality. Collaborations in endless progress, spanning many years, whole eras of childhood within the institution, erasing the vicious tribal and secular divisions of the student body, in order to laud and celebrate, with incredible unity of vision, two subjects,

two aesthetic values, that were among the most un-
speakable in our open society, and which would, if they
emerged in such, be swiftly punished with violence and
hygienic expulsion. I remember, tinged with guilt, what
occurred under these great tapestries, in the illumination of a special quality of piercing grey Scottish light,
filtered through the dusty mottled glass, and opening up
the yawning, oppressive heights of the twin Victorian
ceilings to the eye. Divided by a beam of heavily var-
nished wood panelling, the ceilings were caked with yellowish rashes of hardened wet paper missiles, formed
in small hands lathered with green carbolic soap, and
loosed onto the plaster above with a practiced swing of
the arm, like a shot from a sling.

The cubicle farthest from the entrance contained the
oldest and most ornate mural. The centrepiece was a
full-length figure of Hitler drawn originally in biro and
pencil on the right-hand wall, so regally tall that the artists would have had to climb up on the cistern to complete the head and other details. Various elements of the
figure had been gone over again in biro, pencil, crayon
and thick marker pen; the moustache and other facial
features, which were beautifully realised as Hitler's sombre grimace of concentrated will, his penetrating eyes,
the swastika armband, the buttons on his uniform, the
eagle badge, and the anachronistic addition of DM boots,
clearly depicted and labelled as such (every community
that takes a foreign god must subject that god to some
minimum of localisation). So many hands and pens of
different persuasions: some childish, experimental or
inept, and self-consciously so in the light-handed, ten-
tative sketch-like lines with which they seemed only to
whisper ghostly suggestions to the leadership of stronger artists. In some instances these suggestions or attempts had been rejected by general consensus and the
stronger pens, as in the case of the early biro addition

of Hitler's erect penis protruding through his uniform. Whilst still only just visible, despite some later efforts to revive the notion, the detail had been muffled and suppressed with erasers, Tipp-ex and saliva, hardened lumps of wet tissue mash, and written over many times with bolder, more assertive lines of ink. This shimmering multitude of lines and hands, suggestions, mistakes and re-markings (not to mention incidental and independent or semi-independent marginalia in the form of figures, drawings and texts) gave this figure of Hitler a breathtakingly textured complexity, and an angelic presence in the cubicle, austere and serene, operating within many mysterious dimensions.

The right arm, with its darkly rendered armband and thick black swastika, was raised in a nazi salute parallel to the faded, overruled penis. The hand at the end of it was perhaps the least unified element of the figure, hands being very difficult to draw well (even the more confident pens had been unable to find a satisfactory shape, resulting in an elongated and ephemeral hand, broken apart in great fractals of ink and chipped plaster). Those who have devoted academic study to the details of Hitler's body, remembered or depicted, found that many, whilst condemning and rejecting Hitler's remarkable eyes and face, have often concluded that he had very perfect and beautiful hands.

The head of the figure was crowned with a halo of nine circumcised penises that emerged like compass points from behind it. The original and first stood central and vertical like a great *axis mundi*, rising from behind the crown of the head and probably intended as a protrusion from the head itself, in mockery of the figure. As others were added in different hands to carefully fill out the halo, the pejorative value of the original was negated and reversed, and even the jets of sperm shooting from some of the phalluses did not detract from the impression of regalia. As with the rest of the figure, each well-formed constituent had been messily traced and shadowed hundreds of times, drawing the phalluses together into a furiously unified and endless circle.

The halo, a great Sun, a foul and awesome celestial disc, signified the majesty of the figure over a dense landscape of rich brown and yellow smears on crumbling plaster, into which was absorbed a thick and ancient odour, held in by forests of spidery swastikas, words and numbers, names and dates, curses, dedications, exhortations, proclamations, confessions, appeals, and devotions. These forests spread into and across the other cubicles, inside which reproductions and revisions of the Hitler figure and its halo were sketched, to different degrees of fidelity, corruption and schism. The original figure had uncountable and unnameable authors, and absorbed the gaze and pen-strokes of endless daily visitors, never more than one at a time. The toilet was a shockingly beautiful and highly functional room, that is to say, inescapable to the students, all of whose routines fed inside, and a high example of the power of art that breathes.

In those years, when I was trying to go to sleep, and my mind had entered the liminal estate of dreamy fragments and carbonated blood – the untidy beginnings of sleep that sometimes overplayed their role and jolted me back to consciousness rather than plunging me deeper as they were charged – I would fall into strange auxiliary organs of that institution. I remember the dizziness of being doubled over in the Cubicle of the Angel of Hitler, and seeing myself from an impossible distance in the tall narrow space (which retained its spatial characteristics despite the absence of its walls, which were suggested by the chalk-drawn outlines of the cuboid), like the soul of the nerve of the root of a tooth deep in the lowest cavity, like a living battery, an organic component in a religious machine, and then I would have the *big-small* thing. There were a number of primitive visual elements, but suddenly, the minuteness of an atom and the vastness of a celestial body were felt, represented more through pulverising sensation than image. And the juxtaposition, back and forth as a switch is flicked, aided the comprehension of such spaces too small and too great to see. I felt the space.

There was for me a diaphanous notion of community in the solitude of the toilet. The subversion of our behaviour there was actually dictated by the room itself, which acquired through the collection of our behaviour, a towering grey agency, that screamed always with a drone of silent cognisance from the wet paper stucco and deeply scarred and beautified walls which we offered in daily worship to it. The first transaction, the first time I ever sold anything for money, took place in the toilet. The item was a creased, black and white topless photograph of Gaynor Goodman from a tabloid newspaper, and the price was a two pence coin. Shortly after this, in the same space, I exchanged a penny and another almost full-page nude photograph that was sexually worthless to me, for a stamp-sized colour image cut neatly from a magazine, depicting the shiny, naked trunk and thin arms of a woman with hanging, bulbous breasts, cut off at the neck and navel. I knew very well what I was buying, I'd already examined the tiny photo in another room where I had tried without success to disguise my excitement from its owner. I took the treasure directly into my cubicle and adhered it to the wall at a respectful height with a piece of wet tissue, where its power instantly caused the murals around it to break apart into water and clouds. Then, and now, I pulled out my hard penis and the sperm shot from its head in silver globules, hanging sublimely in the air like dust.

My descent from the peaks, I remember, was forlorn and mournfully beautiful. I'd recovered the dirty rags of my trousers and nothing else, and my body was crusted with dried blood and earth. My mouth was a dry and evil-smelling wound, and thirst had made it the centre of my body (I availed myself of its smell by pushing air out with my rolled tongue against my palm, which I had licked, and inhaling through my nose at the same time).

I negotiated my course down slowly and pragmatically, using fronds and branches as grips, sticking to the bare earth where possible and crawling on hands and knees when necessary. I had no idea of time, its moorings having been ripped out and away, but the chilly grey light evoked early morning. As my senses returned and located me firmly where I was under the dense perpetual canopy with its shut-in stench of muddy life and frustration, I was struck by a marked sense of actuality, and immediacy. This was the return of the very mechanism of time. I reached out – extended my arm and unfolded my fingers, to feel the nearest, cleanest leaves and their latex veins, and I heard the wonderful sound of water on stone. Glorious water was running down through a snaking network of rocks, cooling the air and offering a way down through the trees.

I lay myself down gently at the water's edge and dipped my face inside. It was a wholesome epiphany. I drank like a dog and rubbed the crystalline liquid all over my face and head, and in my excitement breathed some in through my nose, coughing it out powerfully – the phlegm of god – it tasted like deep caves underground. Still coughing, I saw a dead fish with its head resting on a stone beside me, the angle of its tail so beautifully dynamic and firm: unyielding to the current moving against it. The fish was small and plump, its flesh had the quality of rubber glass tinted with pomegranate. It was so exquisitely evolved, its form was so miraculous and complete, offered on its plate of rock with the glorious water running under it, I knew it was a trap. Betrayed and salivating, I tried not to look at the fish.

I took an inventory of my physical damage. There were three lumps on my head, almost painless, unlike the jarred patch of inflammation behind my right ear, which felt like a glandular infection. It was hot to the touch. Both my eyebrows were cut. My eyelids were dry, like burning sand on my eyeballs. My nose felt sensitive and swollen, and my moustache was a rough and dead appendage that pleaded to be torn off. My lips were cut, raw and horribly dry from sucking bits of wood and other props. My tongue was cursed with a fringe of stinging ulcers. I had a headache. There was an acute pain in my spine between my shoulder blades that spread upwards to the base of my skull and out the sides into both shoulder joints. There was a malignant stimulation in my nipples. My ribs were bruised. It was hard to tell how much skin had been lost around my trunk because dirt and matter were rubbed and worked into it so thoroughly. My hip joints ached painfully. My genitalia, withdrawn into its crevice and covered over by the brown fabric of my trousers, felt like the usual mess of ulcerated sponge and uric squid meat. My knees were skinned and stinging, and below this acute surface damage, the joints themselves were alive with a deep ache in parallel with my hips. My feet were swollen and the skin between each toe was split as though nipped with a razor. The gathering up of my wounds like this allowed me to find a helpful perspective on my achievement. With the water spitting and bubbling against my cheek (my head was still slightly in the stream), and the fish lying disappointed in the periphery of what was now occurring, I took out my hardening penis and began to stroke it off, the queasy lust running and wriggling inside my heart.

Pain and anxiety can be equally met with concentration. No other topography is as generous in facility of this. I do what I've learnt to do again, on my own, throughout these yawning months. I do it all the time. I close my eyes very gently and deliberately. I feel each constituent of my body simultaneously, and disengage the harmonic connections between these physical parts and my consciousness. I gain a new unity as disembodied sensation, the smell of earth and leaves, and then only sound, which itself withdraws discreetly as I become a body of stagnant water, like a sort of rock-pool, covered with velvet-green algal mats earned through degrees of sincerity, the regalia of still life. The pains in my neck and back become contours of the pool's bottom: *its* spine, the warm urine I release without tension or effort is a thick, oily discharge from a vein in the earth below, a mineral bile, conditioning this corpus of green water, helping to further soften the flakes of bark and spiny, wooden fingers that drift glacially along precise and minute courses, feeling out the extent of its dimension. If my body jerks or I move or presume to rearrange myself to even the slightest extent, these pieces of twig are broken apart like fibrous rust, and cause currents of movement through the water that disturb its covering plates of algae, and the privacy of my stillness, my absence.

There it is.

I'd like you to imagine this image being pierced by rusty barbed hooks around the bottom. The hooks are yanked sharply by crusted lengths of twine that smell of seawater and greasy bacon rind, and they tear the bottom right out. It disintegrates into singed fragments of rice-paper, and we fall down smoothly through this compromise and multiply out, dissipating and becoming indistinguishable from the air, which is hot and dark, and becomes very black, and then lost of any quality as it's sucked down into a wide iron vent in a great breath that draws in forever.

I think, that I've become so dedicated a medium of images that I can no longer live fully. Like an earthworm, I consume and excrete simultaneously and continuously, within the same act as moving. My consumption propels me forward. Masturbation is a feminine act. Within the cell, in my retreat, the sexual act is inverted: the image asserts itself over me, and I masturbate not *to* it, but *under* it. It is hard, permanent and clarified, still without mercy, and I flutter around it toothlessly, like the efforts of a mosquito at a statue of marble, it yields nothing other than the vision of its Apollonian appendages.

I often think, since I've started writing, that I am simply thrown in life from one image to the next; moreover the mundane and uncharged motions between these tableaux are simply their elements and themes in the process of being gathered together and broken apart. The truth of things is that which is revealed to me through symbols and emblems that I recognise, or are familiar with enough to interpret. As for the templates into which these fit, however fleetingly, their subtleties, and their difficulties, these were handed to me. Maybe the only part that is truly mine, is the coloured wash through it all. Even I myself could never mix the primaries together with quite the same balance ever again. I love colour and light very deeply. The wash, this colour, through this image and in my greater world, is the colour of prostitution.

Hours beyond daybreak, and the sun has established the lodge firmly in the weight of its heat, the smell of damp wood baking giving way to earth and rustically perfumed air as I push open the door and walk outside into the privilege and the glory. I am wearing my unwashed gardening trousers and a brown chequered shirt, in the pocket of which are some coins of money, with which I look forward to purchasing a chicken in the village.

Winding down through the trees I hear a woman's heavy sob amongst the birdsong. I turn into the wide dirt passage that leads out of the orchard, with its perfect walls of green bamboo, the swarms of tiny leaves meeting overhead to form a tall canopy, closing the artery into a tunnel of gently filtered light. The tunnel is scented and visually punctuated by several enormous jackfruit rotting on the vine. Three or so are lying there shamelessly on the red dirt, connected by their rope-like branch, another two or more hanging heavily down through the bamboo leaves from the tree above. (The scent of rotting flesh that lingers around the entrance, which I breathe in deeply whenever I glide under the archway on my bike, is in truth not the product of these jackfruits alone, but also the deep, rusted tin barrel filled permanently with waste from the house of Goodly's daughter.)

Aunty Goodly is sat like a sodden, folded mattress, limbs splayed, propped up only by her spine and the blubber around it, at the extremity of the passage, underneath the largest of the hanging fruits. She is crying without restraint, and I see the tear streaks down her chubby cheeks glistening in the sunlight as I walk cautiously towards her. The jackfruit hangs above her precariously, like a bloated corpse in a gibbet, sap weeping in thin strings from fly-veiled wounds; a signature, a halo over the scene, a cosmological chandelier at the head of the bamboo corridor, behind, and thus reserved for those inside, the rotting archway of old carved wood and jealous ivy that makes the entrance to Auntie Goodly's orchard. (I feel a trivial sense of risk when I ride under this heavy spiked mass, which we have no choice but to do, and though I enjoy the risk and the smell and especially the spectacle of the hanging lump, which is capable sometimes of giving me a nostalgic erection when the flies and the light cause it to evoke the romance of Wallachian gore, I often fantasise about shooting it down with Goodly's revolver, impressing everyone, and seducing her with the impression that I am truly an *able-bodied man*.)

Her black gaze meets mine through the dust and shafts of coppery sunlight. The viscous mask of her tears, in association with the taut nostrils and contorted mouth, feminises and ennobles her distress. I walk over, and reach out my hand to touch her face as she howls breathily up at me, and I am ready to swoon and collapse with the intensity of these gestures, with the alertness of my heart. I feel the viscosity of those tears with my fingers in envy, stroking her course cheek, the fringe of her short haircut brushing my swollen knuckles, the bruises nearly as black as her eyes. The mess of her gaze reconfigures itself slightly on my wounds and I feel her curiosity fighting against the current of her pain. Choking, she tells me the simple, stark, understandable reason.

Here this woman is: fat and murderous, scabby-kneed, full of wind and poison. And crying wet viscous tears that are rolling down past her neckline. Her little tits, her wet little cups, are absolutely meaningless to me. I feel the same way I did when she told me about her murder.

She pulls me down to herself.

I feel the meat-flower of her foreign breath on my eye. In her needy uneasy embrace is the new charity of the trees and the earth of the orchard; the lodge is mine again, after all and forever. But the time has come to move from here, which has become like a collection of photographs to me. My early career in anthropology has been in error. I would like the chance to truly embrace poverty, solitude and the pain of my conditions without medicinal armour, I want to defect permanently to the deep blue East, to breathe wind and petrol, to eat wild flowers.

NEW JUCHE is the nom de guerre of a writer and photographer who lives and works in Southeast Asia. He is also the author of *Wasteland*, *The Mollusc* and *Gymnasium*.

Made in the USA
Middletown, DE
05 February 2021